Construction Tendering

CONSTRUCTION TECHNOLOGY AND MANAGEMENT

A series published in association with the Chartered Institute of Building.

This series will, when complete, cover every important aspect of construction. It will be of particular relevance to the needs of students taking the CIOB Member Examinations, Part 1 and 2, but will also be suitable for degree courses, other professional examinations, and practitioners in building, architecture, surveying and related fields.

Project Evaluation and Development
Alexander Rougvie

Practical Building Law
Margaret Wilkie with Richard Howells

Building Technology (3 volumes)
Ian Chandler
   Vol. 1 Site Organisation and Method
   Vol. 2 Performance
   Vol. 3 Design, Production and Maintenance

The Economics of the Construction Industry
Geoffrey Briscoe

Construction Management (2 volumes)
Robert Newcombe, David Langford and Richard Fellows
   Vol. 1 Organisation Systems
   Vol. 2 Management Systems

Construction Tendering
Andrew Cook

CONSTRUCTION TENDERING

Theory and Practice

Andrew E. Cook

B.T. Batsford Ltd · London

in association with the Chartered Institute of Building

Typeset by Deltatype Ltd, Ellesmere Port, Cheshire
and printed in Great Britain by
Dotesios Ltd Trowbridge, Wilts

Published by B T Batsford Limited
4 Fitzhardinge Street, London W1H 0AH

A CIP catalogue record for this book is
available from the British Library

ISBN 0 7134 6228 0

Contents

Acknowledgement

The author and publisher are grateful to the Royal Institution of Chartered Surveyors for permission to quote from SMM7 General Rule 10, page 14; The Chartered Institute of Building for questions from past examination papers on Quantity Surveying and Estimating; and RIBA Publications for JCT 80 Amendment 7.

1 The Building Environment

Type and nature of the industry

Economic environment

The construction industry operates within a complex economic system. This system incorporates both private and public productive activity and is therefore a mixed economy.[1] The conservative government of the eighties has tried to reduce spending in the public sector by various methods including the controversial privatisation progamme. Even so, statistics published by the Central Statistical Office (CSO) show that the public sector is quite substantial as it accounted for over 40% of the gross national product in 1986.[2] Transfer payments such as social security and national debt interest account for about half of this figure.

A number of industries representing numerous organisations carry out production which supports the economy. These industries can be broadly described as being *industrial*, *commercial* and *service*. There are three types of production in which industry is engaged and these are known as *primary*, *secondary* and *tertiary*:[3]

primary production involves the extracting or harnessing of natural resources such as mining, quarrying, farming, forestry, fishing and energy supply

secondary production involves manufacturing products from natural resources such as vehicles, clothing, food, drink, tobacco, machinery, concrete, bricks, windows and construction*

tertiary production involves the provision of services such as banking, insurance, transportation, distribution, communications, legal, entertainment and architectural design.

Statistics show that in 1986 just over 2% of the working population in Great Britain were employed in primary production, 27% in secondary and 71% in tertiary production. These and other figures for the construction industry are constantly changing due to changes in both the demand for construction work and the attitude of the workforce. For example, the time of year generally deter-

---

* This is in accordance with the Standard Industrial Classification 1980.

mines the start of construction, usually in spring. To some extent the industry is seasonal because many workers seek alternative work inside during the winter months and return when the weather is milder.

Size of the industry   The construction industry is an important part of the national economy as statistics show. In 1986 it employed approximately 1.5 million people, nearly 3% of the total working population. This represents 10.5% of those employed in secondary production. The figure is inclusive of administrative, professional, technical and clerical staff along with those that are self employed. The figure does not include those involved with the large network of manufacturers and merchants that supply the building materials and components. In addition, the industry turnover of £30,123m at that time was 6% of the gross national product.

Scope of work   The construction industry can be summarised as one which provides a wide range of work by a variety of organisations for different employers. It incorporates both building and civil engineering, two distinct parts of the industry responsible for different types of construction work. They operate under separate regulations and employ their own brand of consultants.

Type of firm	% of firms	% of operatives	% of total employees	% of output (approx)	Value of output £million
General builders	39.80	32.68	34.35	33	2157.4
Building & civil engineering	2.20	14.77	14.04	16	1009.2
Civil engineering	1.66	6.82	5.58	7	484.3
Specialist trades	56.34	45.73	46.03	44	2875.6
				Total	6526.5

Table 1.1   Employment and output of private contractors in 1986, July–September period; by type of firm
Source: *Housing and Construction Statistics**

* These and other statistics such as contractors' output by region are published quarterly.[4] They are of particular importance in their contribution to marketing strategy.[5] Firms are able to identify both the regions and the type of work in which they may concentrate their production activity. Note that such trends are only a guide as they are historic.

Civil engineering is concerned with the construction, maintenance and repairing of the infrastructure, whereas building accounts for all other building activity. Both deal with major and minor projects and some projects consist of a combination of both building and civil engineering work. Private construction firms consist of general builders, building and civil engineering contractors, civil engineering contractors and a host of specialist traders or sub-contractors such as plasterers, plumbers, electricians and glaziers. Some of these specialists are subsidiaries of both building and civil engineering organisations. The proportion of the industry which they represent is shown in table 1.1.

There also exists direct service organisations (DSOs), formerly referred to as direct labour organisations and public works departments. They are in a way the public sector equivalent to private firms.[6] Their output accounted for just over 10% of total construction output in 1986 compared with 12% in 1976. The DSOs are departments within local authority, responsible for carrying out building work in a similar way to private organisations. Because of the need to maintain local authority building stock, including emergency repairs, in addition to bricklayers, joiners and labourers the workforce includes plasterers, plumbers and the like. Whilst being part of local authority, their accounts are kept separate from those of other departments.

The scale of building work undertaken by different sized firms ranges from the fitting of a door lock to a multi-million pound development. Correspondingly, there are different levels of expertise and finance required by these firms. This can be observed from table 1.2, which represents all types of private contractors in the industry.

In this table the size of firm is based on the number of people employed. As to what constitutes small, medium and large is to some extent a matter of opinion. However, in 1987 out of the industry's top one hundred construction firms only four employed less than 600 people. Those four were in the bottom ten of the group.[7]

Size of firm	Percentage of firms	Number of employees per firm	Percentage of output (approx.)	Value of output £million
Small	90.00	1 – 7	28	1746.7
Medium	9.94	8 – 599	52	3498.6
Large	0.06	600 and over	20	1281.2
			Total	6526.5

*Table 1.2   Employment and output of private contractors in 1986,
July–September period; by size of firm*
Source: *Housing and Construction Statistics*

At the lower level the industry is very labour intensive. As only a limited amount of small plant and tools are required, easily bought or hired, it is not surprising that this is one of the easiest industries in which to set up business. This is also a contributing factor to the high proportion of small firms that exist.

Statistics by the DoE show that since 1979 there has been a growth in repair and maintenance work which in 1985 had risen to 46% of the total industry output. With this increase and the decline in the number of major projects during the late seventies and early eighties many large firms formed economically viable departments to capitalise on the expansion of the market in smaller contracts, particularly housing repair and maintenance (see table 1.3). This has resulted in greater competition for medium sized firms.

Type of work   The different types of work undertaken by the construction industry are as follows:

BUILDING

General new building work – buildings such as hospitals, houses, offices, factories and supermarkets are constructed entirely as new

Alteration work – work carried out to existing buildings. It is a broad term that covers specific types of work such as:

> *Conversion* – change of building use, eg a large house converted to flats or a home for the elderly

> *modernisation or rehabilitation* – change of building character, eg installation of central heating system or replacement of antiquated bathroom suite

> *extension* – change of building size, eg an additional room built onto the side of a house

> *alteration* – change of building formation, eg removal of a dividing wall to form one large room from two small rooms

> *maintenance work* – work carried out to replace or repair defective parts of an existing building such as rotted timber window frames or loose roof tiles

> *demolition work* – existing structures such as dilapidated factories are removed to make way for modern industrial estates

CIVIL ENGINEERING

Construction activity, other than building, such as bridges, roads, dams and canals. The activity covers new work, alterations maintenance and demolition.

Projects generally fall within one of these categories although some may relate to a number of them.

Market sectors The construction industry is segregated into market sectors in accordance with both the type of work undertaken and the sectors of the economy to which they relate. These sectors are shown in table 1.3.

As housing repair and maintenance is given as one figure it is not possible to say exactly what proportion of total output relates to public and private work. Assuming that private housing repairs and maintenance are in the same proportions as those for public, then private work accounts for over 59% of total industry output.

Type of work	Sector of economy		Output value £m	% of new work (approx)	% of all work (approx)
NEW WORK					
Housing:	Private		4697	29	16
	Public		842	5	3
Other:	Private:	Industrial	2632	16	9
		Commercial	4226	26	14
	Public		3888	24	13
			16286		54
REPAIR AND MAINTENANCE					
Housing:	Private and Public		7427	54	24
Other:	Private		2642	19	9
	Public		3768	27	12
			13837		46

Table 1.3   Construction output of private contractors and DSOs in 1986; by market sector
Source: *Housing and Construction Statistics*

These figures reflect the strength of private industry investment which accounts for 71% of all new construction work undertaken. A strong demand from private house buyers and commercial institutions is indicated.

In contrast to this the public sector requirement for new housing has halved since 1980. Their main concern is the maintenance of large property stocks. Despite this a large proportion of outstanding repairs are unlikely to be carried out, especially to the structurally unsound high rise blocks of the sixties. As there is little chance of more public money becoming available such property may have to be demolished if it cannot be sold to the private sector.

High risk Construction is a very competitive high risk industry governed strongly by economic, political, legal, social and environmental issues. This is very apparent from the number of insolvencies of construction firms as shown in figure 1.1. It is difficult to link conclusively insolvencies with economic decline or growth although there appears to be some correlation. A factor behind such trends may be the combination of the equilibrium between firms entering and leaving the industry and the prevailing economic climate.

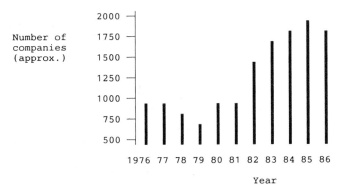

Figure 1.1 *Insolvencies of construction firms 1976–86; England and Wales*
Source: *Housing and Construction Statistics*

By the late seventies the majority of weaker firms had left the industry and the new firms had to be strong to contemplate entry. This coupled with the fact that the slump in output had eased may explain the fall in the number of insolvencies up to 1979. After 1979, maybe due to the economic recovery of the eighties, the number of firms entering the industry annually increased significantly. In 1986 there were 171,660 firms in the industry compared to 101,080 in 1979, an increase of nearly 70%. It is therefore inevitable that insolvencies will rise accordingly.

Another contributing factor was the almost static tender levels, on average, from mid 1980 to early 1987. Throughout this period building costs continued to rise rapidly. Some builders were affected more than others due to regional variations that occurred above and below the average. Builders absorbed these increases by reducing their mark-up for overheads and profit.

Divided economy   Due to the economic and political problems of the seventies and the austerity of the eighties many changes have taken place in the economy. During the period of economic recession many old and marginal industries disappeared, bringing mass unemployment to many parts of the country. Since then there has been a gradual improvement in the economy and new industries have emerged, bringing new economic and social opportunities. Existing industries have generally become more competitive. However, as a result of this what is commonly known as the North-South Divide has been created.

The construction industry has not escaped the effects of this phenomenon. Unlike other regions, construction output in the South East was not only maintained but increased to almost saturation levels by the mid-eighties. In 1986 the region accounted for 40% of total output in Britain. Both the shortage of manpower and the glut of work available in this area has resulted in artificially high salaries and building prices. The encouraging news for the industry in 1987 was that other regions were experiencing higher output. Ironically, this may to an extent be due to the South East overspill, part of which has been caused by the housing problems in this area: shortages of labour, materials and building land, their respective high cost and the inflated property prices.

There is a strong possibility that the split in the industry may increase after 1992 due to the forming of the single European market,[8] intended to remove national frontiers, along with the completion of the Channel Tunnel in 1993. This is because the majority of increased trading in Britain is likely to polarise around London.

Construction abroad   The construction industry extends beyond the United Kingdom as British contractors carry out a substantial amount of construction work throughout the world. In obtaining this work they face fierce competition from each other; those native to each particular country that offers work and those from foreign countries other than Britain. The amount of work carried out abroad is shown in table 1.4. Within each region the volume of work varies each year. Generally this does affect a region's proportion of the total work carried out abroad. This is also the case for the Economic Community and Europe as their output figures deviated in 1986 due to changes in EEC country membership. The majority of British construction activity, over 70%, is concentrated in the Middle East in Asia, Rest of Africa and the Americas.

The total amount of construction work abroad provides employment for many people although the movement of skilled workers is generally restricted to Europe and Asia. These regions passively acted as very important sanctuaries for many skilled workers during the declining British construction industry in the late seventies.

Region	1983 £m	1984 £m	1985 £m	1986 £m	% of total in 1986
European Community	24	21	45	79	3.59
Rest of Europe	80	58	57	23	1.04
Middle East in Asia	669	675	700	585	26.55
Rest of Asia	264	306	305	261	11.85
Middle East in Africa	62	66	48	81	3.68
Rest of Africa	524	557	482	381	17.30
Americas	436	440	611	594	26.96
Oceania	255	217	237	199	9.03
All countries	2,314	2,340	2,485	2,203	

Table 1.4   Value of British construction work overseas, 1983–86; by region
Source: *Housing and Construction Statistics*

Type of clients

The construction industry carries out work for a variety of clients. These clients are either from the public sector or the private sector as indicated in table 1.3 and are often referred to as employers, especially as it is the term used in standard forms of contract.
   Typical public sector clients are:

   central government – represented by the Property Services Agency (PSA), responsible for government buildings and those of the armed forces

   local government – represented by local authorities

   nationalised industries – represented by British Rail, British Steel and the like

   public corporations – represented by health authorities and the like.

Typical private sector clients are:

   financial institutions – represented by banks and building societies *industrial organisations* – represented by manufacturing firms and the like

commercial individuals – represented by the public other than businesses

religious and charitable organisations – represented by churches, aid organisations and housing charities.

Public sector clients They are accountable for public funds and are therefore constrained in the way they procure construction work. They are all bound by statute and are greatly influenced by government policy. Some operate their own form of contract although local authorities use standard forms.

A typical constraint on local authorities is that central government determines the cost limits within which they operate. Also, prior to government legislation in 1980 local authorities were free to award contracts to their DSOs without any form of competition. This practice was curbed and from April 1981 DSOs had to compete with private firms for local authority and other public work as shown in table 1.5. However, since April 1989 the situation has been amended and DSOs now have to compete for all contracts.

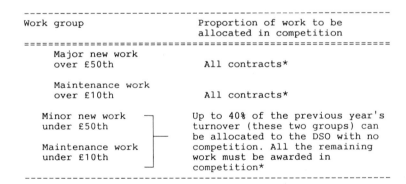

Work group	Proportion of work to be allocated in competition
Major new work over £50th	All contracts*
Maintenance work over £10th	All contracts*
Minor new work under £50th ⎤ ⎟ Maintenance work under £10th ⎦	Up to 40% of the previous year's turnover (these two groups) can be allocated to the DSO with no competition. All the remaining work must be awarded in competition*

Table 1.5   Allocation of local authority work; by work group Legislation: Planning and Land Act 1980, 28 July 1988 amendment
Source: *Leeds City Council*

* DSOs and private firms are allowed to tender. Separate accounts are kept by DSOs for major, minor and maintenance work. The reason for this is that if a DSO records a loss in any of the three accounts the government has the power to prevent them carrying out future work in that particular group.

Constraints also arise from a council's own regulations such as the Local Authority Goods and Services Act 1970. This limits the work that DSOs can undertake as it prohibits them from private sector work although they may work for authorities other than their own. In addition to this restriction DSOs are prohibited from employing labour-only sub-contractors.

Other policies that are adopted by various local authorities which affect tendering for work are summarised as follows:

priority given to local firms – protection of local industry

open tendering – creation of greater competition and equal opportunities

minimum number of firms tendering – creation of competition and prevention of allegations suggesting foul play

discretion of the council – decisions, especially those relating to the way tenders are obtained and awarded, are at the discretion of councillors.

Private sector clients　　They can be more flexible in their approach to selecting a contractor and the related contractual arrangements as they are generally only accountable to themselves or their shareholders. Finance for construction work is generated from either internal funds or external borrowing.

Large organisations may be governed by policies contained in their articles of constitution although such policies are unlikely to interfere with sound commercial decision making. This flexibility does not extend to all private clients, for example they may choose only to employ firms with which they do business or deal only with one firm:

a bank may select building firms that have an account with them – to maintain business relations

a large chain store may employ a contractor to carry out all building requirements throughout the country – to maintain established standards.

Further, the future generation of clients is likely to consist of a greater foreign representation than that at present. This is inevitable as more companies from abroad decide to infiltrate the single European market and those currently operating within cross the dismantled frontiers not only to facilitate expansion but also take advantage of new potentially lucrative market sectors. Such changes are already taking place in Britain as evidenced firstly by the number of major Japanese car manufacturers that are building assembly lines in Britain and secondly by the number of successful companies that have been bought by larger European organisations that do not already operate within an EEC member state.

These new clients are likely to prefer the procurement methods for building work to which they are familiar as opposed to current methods offered by the British building industry. At best a compromise between methods may emerge. Those within the building industry, together with their clients, will undoubtedly be interested in the level of success achieved by such practices. Whatever the success of alternative procurement methods they must be welcomed if only to provide an objective measure of the quality and value of service currently delivered by the industry.

Client and industry requirements

Diversity of needs　　There are many aspects of building that a client may consider such as initial cost, running and maintenance costs, location, size, style, appearance, shape, quality. Each client considers these differently in accordance with their own organisation's strategy.

Because of the different types of client, the wide range of building work they require, the various regions in which they are based and the changing environment in which they operate, there is no one ideal building solution that will suit all clients. Some clients prefer a low initial building cost and higher running and maintenance costs due to limited finances or because the building is only required for a few years.

Light manufacturing and high-tech industries are attracted to modern industrial estates whereas supermarkets may be situated in town centres with larger complexes moving out to the suburbs. Offices and shops in city centres are being designed to help maintain the character of the area concerned. There is also a trend towards the use of traditional brickwork instead of concrete to external facades. However, all clients do require a value for money functional building produced on time.

Value for money means that the client pays the market price for the work he receives. Thus, when a client wishes to spend ten million pounds on a building he neither wants to spend less on an inferior building nor receive a building which is worth less.

Functional building means fully operational. Thus the structure should be sound and free from water penetration, heating and ventilation systems should be effective and free from constant breakdowns.

Produced on time means the client takes possession of the completed building, fully functional, on the required date. This is of particular importance to clients who have planned to take possession in time to take advantage of high seasonal business such as the

Christmas shopping period or the demand for holiday accommodation during the summer months.

Level of performance The industry deals with a product that cannot be mass produced in factory conditions but nevertheless has an expected life span longer than many other commodities and actually appreciates in value. Even so, many clients consider the construction industry to have failed client requirements. Some contractors may be to blame but the majority are reputable firms that endeavour to carry out their obligations to a high standard.

Contractors often have to build in accordance with architect's design drawings using the materials specified and the labour available, all of which to a varying degree are outside their control. For instance, whilst the supervision of labour is the sole responsibility of the contractor on large sites where many operatives are employed, there must be a degree of reliance on the integrity of tradesmen to carry out the work in a proper manner.

Considering the number of contractors between 1976 and 1986 that obtained work by reducing or even eliminating their profit margins the industry has given good value for money. Another factor in support of this view is that since 1974 the price of labour and materials has increased at a much higher rate than the value of contractors' tenders[9] even though part of this was made possible due to increased efficiency in the industry. Any inefficiency that did exist was no worse than that of the industry's clients.

EEC and government influence

The EEC In 1992 the European Economic Community (EEC) will remove national frontiers and trade restrictions to form one large economic market. The twelve member EEC countries are to be represented by a parliament, based in Brussels, responsible for legislation and rationalisation of practice and procedures. If all barriers are removed, which is doubtful, the market will provide greater opportunities for both contractors and construction operatives. However, competition between firms from the various EEC countries will become very intensive. Because the new market will be so large, fierce competition is also likely to come from countries outside the EEC, especially the USA and Japan.

The Japanese may provide the greatest competitive source irrespective of whether a single European market is formed. Their industry is larger than that of either the EEC or USA and they have already penetrated the British market.[10] The reluctance of Japanese contractors to construct from details produced by independent consultants could impede their progress. However, many clients prefer contractors to provide a complete design and build service.

The government The fluctuating output of the construction industry is in the form of peaks and troughs containing mini peaks and troughs. Thus, during a rising trend in demand there are small intermittent rises and falls in demand. This is because the output of the industry is sensitive to changes in the economy. The government plays a major role in influencing construction output by regulating the supply of and demand for construction work.

The supply of construction work is controlled in the public sector through changes in government and local authority spending. Through the eighties the government imposed reductions in local authority housing budgets which resulted in a fall in the construction of new council houses.

The demand for construction work is controlled by increasing the cost of such work to the client. An indirect method is to vary bank lending rates. High lending rates for house buyers, local authorities and industry reduces their spending power. A more direct method is to vary taxes and grants. Taxation on capital gains, property income and value added tax (VAT) on construction work have a negative effect on the viability of a project, whereas property improvement grants have a positive effect. Local authority grants and incentives for businesses to set up in particular regions also have a positive affect by increasing an organisation's capacity to spend on construction. Other factors such as government policy or market forces also affect the industry:

> The Conservative government's determination to increase home ownership expanded demand in the private sector during the eighties and was further fuelled by low lending rates. This was possible due to a sustained period of low inflation together with the introduction of competition for business between banks and building societies. By the end of the decade demand fell due to high inflation and interest rates.

> The formation of the Housing Action Trust (HATS) with its power to take possession of proportions of local authority housing and offer it to the private sector. In 1988 Leeds city council lost about 8% of housing stock to HATS.

> The government's concern for increased efficiency and greater competition prompted them to introduce the 1980 Planning and Land Act, and subsequent amendments, which requires DSOs to compete for work.

> Increased demand for construction within the economy since 1986 has resulted in tender prices rising faster than costs. This

trend is evident in the South East but does not apply equally to regions nationally.

The commencement of the channel tunnel project is an example of a joint venture by two governments and private industry. By uniting to undertake this project the participants have provided a boost to the industry.

However, to enable the industry to maintain its capacity and operate both effectively and efficiently, better control of construction demand is required. This warrants an investigation by both government and industry representatives to consider possible measures that would reduce sensitivity to economic changes and create a more even flow of work.

The building process

This section relates to building and not civil engineering although whilst the titles of parties responsible for carrying out some functions are different the process for each is very similar.

When a client requires building work to be carried out he contacts an organisation within the industry. The two most common approaches by a client are to obtain the services of either a building contractor or a consultant such as an architect or quantity surveyor.

Approaching a builder direct is the usual course of action for home owners requiring a kitchen extension or a house of standard design, and is also gaining popularity with more ambitious clients who are responding to the sophisticated packages now on offer. However, they rely fully on the integrity of the builder to carry out satisfactory work at a reasonable price. In other circumstances a client normally approaches an architect who will then select a suitable builder. A contractor may be chosen to negotiate a price for the work or alternatively asked to submit a price in competition with other contractors of similar standing.[11]

Stages within the process   There are a number of stages that take place between inception and completion of a project.[12] The pattern is common to most types of projects although in some cases certain stages are either omitted, varied or merged together depending on the method used for selecting the contractor. The stages take place during the design, tendering and building periods.

The following summary highlights these stages, with those for the design period generally representing the Royal Institute of British Architects (RIBA) plan of work:

DESIGN PERIOD

Brief: **Inception** – Appointment of architect; client brief to convey building needs such as location, shape, size and function. Limits on cost, time or appearance are important factors that must be identified

Feasibility – Site investigations and enquiries to statutory bodies, etc, will be carried out to help formulate development potential and any restrictions that may exist. The architect will also appoint a quantity surveyor and specialist engineers unless the size and type of project does not warrant this.

Viability is established; likely cost and appearance of the building are provided

Sketch plans: **Outline proposals** – Outline drawings of possible schemes are produced to comply with the brief; cost implications are monitored; the most appropriate scheme is chosen

Scheme design – The chosen design is developed further; the specification for the project and engineering designs are introduced; cost for each part of the building are produced and targets set

Once the scheme design is approved additional fees will be charged for any subsequent changes instigated by the client

Working drawings: **Detailed design** – All decisions relating to design are finalised and checked to ensure they are within the financial targets set

Once the detailed design is approved any subsequent changes will create additional work for the design team

Production information – All work is finalised to enable construction work to be carried out. This includes final working drawings, specifications and a form of contract. Where applicable, documents are prepared and builders are selected to enable a competitive price to be obtained

TENDERING PERIOD

Contractor selection: **Issue of documents** – Selected contractors are issued with the same information upon which to base their price and are allowed the same amount of time to submit a tender

Preparation
of tender: **Estimate** – The net cost of building work is prepared by the builder

Tender – Management converts the net cost into a tender by adding company overheads and profit. The final amount, termed the tender sum or value of bid, is submitted to the architect

BUILDING PERIOD
Building
process: **Site work** – Contractor carries out building work in accordance with the drawings and specification and within the time stipulated in the contract

Project supervision – Architect ensures that the work is carried out correctly in relation to work, workmanship and materials. Instructions to vary, increase or delete work may be issued during this period

Site supervision – Contractor is responsible for his operatives and has a duty to carry out the work to the required standard

Interim payments – Contractor is paid regularly for work done, usually monthly. Such monies, determined by the quantity surveyor and sanctioned by the architect, are less a percentage which is retained until the work is completed satisfactorily.

Structure of a building contractor's organisation

The structure of a building contractor's organisation varies between companies due to their respective independent development. There are many factors influencing the various formations and these factors are outlined in the following text.

Types of building contracting organisations   The manner in which organisations may be grouped together is dependant upon the purpose for which it is required. The criteria for distinction is based on a combination of the following:

Type of work   General contractor, specialist subcontractor, speculative builder, labour only sub-contractor

Business unit	Partnership, limited company, DSO, sole trader
Size of firm	Turnover, number of employees*, size of projects
Market location	Local, regional, national, international.

Table 1.6 shows contractor **A** to be the largest firm by turnover whereas contractor **B** is the largest by both number of employees and maximum value of single contracts undertaken. At the other end of the scale contractor **D** is the smallest of the group by turnover and maximum value of jobs undertaken.

Measure	Firm A	Firm B	Firm C	Firm D
Turnover (£m)	100	60	45	13
Number of employees	600	1300	320	450
Max. value of jobs undertaken (£m)	45	90	27	1

Table 1.6 Comparison of size between British building contractors in 1985; by alternative measures
Source: *Building contractors*

However, contractor **C** is the smallest by number of employees. Whilst contractor **B** has the potential to be the largest contractor, because of the capacity to undertake larger jobs than the others, they are unable to attain the level of turnover achieved by contractor **A**. Thus, measuring by value of turnover seems the most appropriate means by which to judge a firms size.

Common constraints Despite the distinctions between organisations there exists a number of core objectives and corporate responsibilities that are common to many firms.[13] Each organisation has its own objectives with different priorities:

---

* This is arguably the least realistic measure as it does not display an organisation's financial and physical ability to operate at a particular level of output. The weakness of the measure is demonstrated in table 1.6 which is formulated from data researched by the author.

Core objectives	*Corporate responsibilities*
Profit maximisation	Shareholders
Service optimisation	Employees
Corporate survival	Clients
Corporate expansion	Creditors

Although listed separately the objectives are linked to the corporate responsibilities. For example, the company has a responsibility to shareholders to maximise profit and strive to attain further growth, although it is argued that profit maximisation is not necessarily the prime motive of all businesses.[14] The objectives and responsibilities of a firm have to be attained if it is to be successful although there are a number of alternative organisational structures that will achieve this.

Tasks to be performed   Irrespective of how an organisation is to be structured there are specific tasks that need to be carried out. A summary of these tasks is as follows:

Office related	*Site related*
Strategic management	Pricing and materials purchase
Accounts	planning
Wages	Cost and contract control
Marketing	Work supervision

The larger the firm the more the tasks are sub-divided and the greater the specialisation of individuals or departments becomes.[15] For smaller firms it is common for each individual to take total responsibility for a number of tasks. For example, in a small firm the person with overall responsibility for managing building work may also have to plan and programme the work or alternatively act as the company's safety officer.

Further, irrespective of the size of firm the duties of specific individuals may vary. For example, one firm may require the quantity surveyor to schedule and order building materials in addition to normal duties.

Typical structure of a smaller firm   Using the tasks as a basis for structuring a typical formation for a small to medium building firm operating from a single office is shown in figure 1.2. Site organisation depends on the size and type of work being undertaken but will include a foreman and maybe trades foremen and gangers. It is not uncommon on large sites to have the contracts manager, quantity surveyor and bonus surveyor based on site. This is especially so for large contractors as they could well have sites located hundreds of miles from head office, therefore they must operate on the basis that each site is self supportive. Communications are maintained by periodic visits from area quantity surveyors who are responsible for overseeing site finance and area contracts managers who are responsible for overseeing site production within budget.

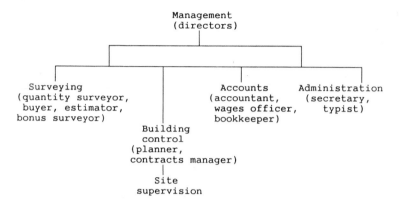

Figure 1.2   Structure of small to medium building firm

Structure of a larger firm   Larger firms tend to have more than one office to enable work within different regions to be carried out more efficiently. Regions may be North and South or East and West. East and West is favoured by some firms because better road and rail links exist North to South.

The structuring of a large firm is similar in principle to that shown for a small to medium firm but with greater vertical and horizontal divisions. Where a firm operates from a number of regional offices and undertakes a variety of work two further levels of hierarchy are introduced to the structuring. This allows structuring to take place in one of two ways, as shown by figures 1.3 and 1.4.

There comes a time when the volume of output for each type of work reaches such large proportions that it becomes more advantageous to have separate specialist companies to deal with the work. This alternative formation, as demonstrated in figure 1.4, is more common as it allows the different expertise to be developed autonomously in order that greater efficiency in each type of work may be achieved.

Both the organisational structure and the company strategy are under constant review in order to meet changing market conditions and clients requirements, whilst also attempting to be one step in front of competitors.

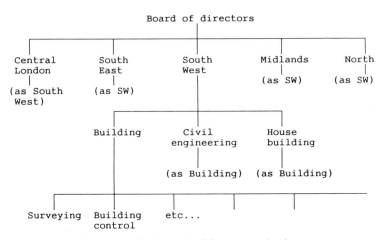

Figure 1.3   Structure of a large building organisation

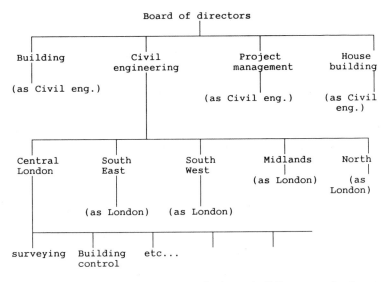

Figure 1.4   Alternative structure of a large building organisation

References

1 HARVEY, J, *Modern economics*, second edition, Macmillan 1974, pp 43.
2 Central Statistical Office, *Annual Abstract of Statistics*, 1988 edition, HMSO, pp 245.
3 HARBURY, C, and LIPSEY, R J, *An introduction to the UK economy*, second edition, Pitman 1986, p 19.
4 Department of the Environment, *Housing and Construction Statistics 1976–86, Great Britain*, HMSO, pp 19, 21–23. sections (b).
5 FISHER, N, *Marketing for the construction industry*, Longmans 1986, pp 114.
6 SEELEY, I H, *Quantity surveying practice*, Macmillan 1984, pp 3–4.
7 The top 100 breakdown, Survey, *Contract Journal*, 2 June 1988, pp 10.
8 PATTISON, M, '1992 and all that', *CQS*, April 1988, pp 36.
9 'Tender prices and building costs', *BCIS News*, no. 20, February 1988.
10 BENNET, J, 'Japanese construction', *CQS*, September 1987, pp 27–8.
11 STONE, P A, *Building economy*, third edition, Pergamon 1983, pp 120–1.
12 CARTLIDGE, D P, and MEHRTENS, I N, *Practical cost planning*, Hutchinson 1982, pp 11–16.
13 HARRIS, F C, and McCAFFER, R, *Modern construction management*, second edition, Granada 1983, pp 156–7.
14 HILLEBRANDT, P M, *Economic theory and the construction industry*, second edition, Macmillan 1985, pp 87–8.
15 BUTLER, J T, *Elements of administration for building students*, third edition, Hutchinson 1982, pp 26–32.

2 Procurement

Parties involved in the construction process

Parties to the contract   A contract for building or civil engineering work is entered into by two parties, namely the client and the contractor. Both parties sign the contract and are therefore bound by the conditions set out therein. The contract must be signed in the presence of and by a third party whose duty is solely to witness the agreement. The contract between the client and the builder is commonly referred to as the *main contract* to differentiate it from other contracts such as those between the builder and his sub-contractors. With, for example, a building contract, the names of the client's quantity surveyor and architect are also written into the document.

In addition, a number of the standard clauses contained in the contract document not only make reference to the client and contractor but also the quantity surveyor, architect, clerk of works, nominated sub-contractors and nominated suppliers. Whilst reference is made to other parties the contract to build is between the client and the building contractor. These other parties enter separate contractual arrangements with either the client or contractor.

Duties and relationships of those involved with the building process   There are various people involved with the building process although their relationship to a contract varies, depending on whether or not their services are mandatory. For instance, the architect is engaged at the discretion of the employer. To protect the rights of both parties it is advisable that some form of agreement is formulated. Such an agreement is closely related to the contract between the client and the contractor.

However, the involvement of the local authority district surveyor (building control officer) is mandatory through legislation.[1] Whilst there is no contract between the local authority and the client or contractor the district surveyor must be allowed to carry out his duties which may include an instruction to alter the building work in order that it complies with the Building Regulations. To this extent the arrangement is related to the contract between the client and the contractor although the local authority cannot be held liable for negligence of their surveyor.

A list of those involved in the building* process is as follows:

Client	Builder	Planning officer
Architect	Estimator	District surveyor
Quantity surveyor	Surveyor	Health and safety inspector
Consultant engineer(s)	Buyer	
Project manager	Planner	
Clerk of works	Contracts manager	
	Site agent	

An outline of the main duties performed by those involved with the building process and their respective inter-relationships is as follows:

Client

The client, or employer, is the most important party in the building process. Without his involvement there would be no need for the services of the others. The client plays an active part in the early stages of the proceedings. Clients who are familiar with the building process may maintain there involvement throughout the remaining periods whilst others tend to leave most matters for the architect to deal with. Initially he is responsible for appointing an architect or other consultant to supervise the whole process on his behalf.

Once the architect is appointed the client is involved in the development of the design. He is required to make interim and final decisions on matters of design and cost, after professional advice has been given. Whilst it is not advised the client often requires many changes to be made in the design throughout the building process.

All documents relating to the contract with a builder must be signed by the client. For matters which may restrict the development of a particular site such as a shared access or adjoining property the client must resolve them himself. This is usually achieved through consultation with a solicitor. Any such problems must be resolved before the building period commences, ideally during the early design period.

When nominated† sub-contractors are used the client signs a separate agreement with them, thus creating a contractual relationship beyond that of the sub-contractor and builder.

As regards finance the client it responsible for all costs associated with the project. These costs will include services relating to local

---

* Building as opposed to civil engineering, hence the term builder is used rather than contractor.

† There are no nominations with the Intermediate Form of contract.

authority Planning and Building Regulation approval, consultancy fees, building costs (contract sum) and any additional costs arising out of the contract due to variations in the work, bona fide claims from the builder and the like. Some of these costs will have to be paid for in full at the time they are incurred whilst others such as building costs are paid in instalments.

Architect

The architect acts on behalf of and for the client. The extent of his responsibilities is dependent on the services he has been commissioned to perform. Where he is engaged from inception to completion of the building process for the designing and supervising of the building work the architect has full control of the proceedings. With local authority contracts the term 'contract administrator', former supervising officer, is used in place of the word 'architect'. Therefore the supervisor of a local authority contract may or may not be an architect.

Initially, the clients needs and requirements must be converted into a viable building solution. The main constraints within which the architect may have to work are function, cost and time. The design must be developed and acceptable to the client as well as satisfy Planning and Building Regulations. Drawings and specifications have to be produced in order to achieve this.

Where the services of a quantity surveyor or consultant engineer is required the architect will advise on their appointment. After their appointment the architect will develop and complete the design in conjunction with the information they provide.

The architect is also responsible for selecting a builder, determining the conditions of his appointment and subsequently supervising his work. During the building period he is responsible for issuing instructions, revised drawings, and certificates for payment plus extensions of time and completion certificates to the contractor. The client is informed of all such events and advised of their cost and time implications.

Copies of letters, drawings, instructions and the like that are issued to one party, for example the builder, must be sent to other interested parties such as the quantity surveyor, consultant engineer, clerk of works and nominated sub-contractors in order that each may carry out their duties in accordance with the contract. Thus the quantity surveyor and clerk of works need copies of any instruction issued to the builder that concern the variation of the work. If for example the instruction relates to ventilation work to be carried out by a nominated sub-contractor then a copy of the instruction will also be issued to that sub-contractor and the consultant services engineer.

Quantity surveyor

The quantity surveyor is appointed to provide the client with advice on building costs and contractual matters throughout the building process, acting as a consultant to the architect. Many quantity surveying practices are also extending their services to specification writing, development appraisal, project management and the like.

Ideally the quantity surveyor should be engaged at the initial stage of design to enable the client to receive the cost advice he needs from the outset. Costs of alternative design solutions are provided whilst the design is developed and more accurate estimates of the likely cost are produced as detailed information is received from the architect.

The quantity surveyor prepares a bill of quantities from the architect's drawings. This document is used as a tender document upon which builders base their tenders. When included as a tendering and contract document the bill of quantities serves as an important cost control document upon which both stage payments and the valuing of variations are based. He also gives advice on selecting builders and suitable contract documents. Once tenders are received then the bill of quantities from the lowest builder's price is checked by the quantity surveyor and if the tender is accepted a cash flow forecast for the client is prepared, based on that tender.

During the building period the quantity surveyor values the work completed to establish the builder's stage payments, values variations to the original design, prepares and agrees the final account with the builder. He may also be required to take charge of nominated sub-contractors' accounts.

Consulting engineer(s)

Consulting engineers and other specialists are responsible to the architect for the design of certain parts of the project and provide information that will assist the quantity surveyor with his financial reporting. Consultants are usually involved in the work carried out by nominated sub-contractors. The extent of involvement by consultants varies. Where there is full responsibility for design and financial control they will select suitable contract conditions for the sub-contractors, value the work for stage payments, variations and final accounts and implement cost control during the building period.

Consultants are involved with structural design, lift, services, electrical, heating and ventilation and other specialised installations.

Project manager

A project manager is appointed by a client to organise and control the whole of the building process on project management contracts.[2] Contracts which are the subject of project management are normally large and of a complex nature.

He is responsible for managing all aspects of the project necessary to provide the client with a value for money functional building, within the financial budget, produced on time. Architects, quantity surveyors, building contractors and others of similar standing may act in the capacity of project manager. On contracts other than project management the title project manager may loosely be used to describe the role of the architect in his supervisory capacity for the client or the contracts manager in his managerial capacity for the builder. However, as project management is now well established the title of project manager should be used exclusively to the manager of such projects to avoid confusion.

Clerk of works

The clerk of works is employed by the client as an inspector to ensure that the builder carries out the work in accordance with the drawings, specification and any further instructions which have been issued by the architect. He performs his duties under the direction of the architect and, under the terms of the contract, the contractor must allow him every reasonable facility to perform his duty. The clerk of works has no power under the contract to issue instructions to the builder on matters for which the architect is responsible unless the architect gives written confirmation within the time stipulated in the contract.

However, on many projects where good relationships are established between the architect and the builder it is common for builders to act on instructions from the clerk of works and seek written instructions later, especially where formal proceedings are likely to delay the progress of the works.

The clerk of works may at times be required to sign daywork sheets submitted by the builder. The signing of such sheets is acknowledgment that the work was carried out in accordance with the details therein. His signature is not an acceptance of either the validity of the daywork sheet or the monies claimed therein.

Many builders may consider the clerk of works to be an unwelcome individual on a building site whilst in fact his presence is of benefit to the builder. To put it crudely, in the course of his duties a keen clerk of works actually looks after the interests of the builder, free of charge, thereby reducing the likelihood of time consuming and costly remedial work.

Builder

The responsibilities of a builder depends on the stage at which he is appointed. When the builder's expertise are required to assist the development of the design his appointment will be early in the design stage. Here, the builder will provide advice on matters of planning, costs, building construction and the integration of services. Unfortunately, the contractors appointment more often than not takes place after the design has been completed, by either negotiation or competitive tendering.

Many builders are extending their traditional role to that of providing clients with advice for proposed developments. The additional services offered include design, technology, finance and cost planning along with those mentioned previously and project management. In addition, contractors are to a varying degree financing projects in a number of ways through joint ventures with clients, variations in the design and build concept[3] and the like.

The builder is responsible for submitting a bona fide tender, signing a contract with the client and carrying out the work, including the organisation and supervision of work to be carried out by sub-contractors, to the architects satisfaction. Separate contracts to that with the client are entered into with the various sub-contractors, whether they are nominated or not. These are referred to as sub-contracts. Agreements are also entered into with suppliers.

Specific tasks are carried out by members of the builders organisation in order that the builder's duties are expedited. These members and their duties are discussed next.

Estimator

The builder's estimator is responsible for pricing building work in accordance with tender documents and to assist management in their submission of a tender to the client or architect as instructed. This includes a report on the project in hand, a summary of project details and a note of any matters of concern.

In order that the implications arising from all aspects of the project are considered he may liaise with the builder's planner, contracts manager, buyer, plant manager and surveyor.* A visit to the proposed site and the architect's office is also necessary in order that this is achieved. Any queries arising from the tender documents are resolved by communicating with either the architect or the quantity surveyor.

It is important that all details and calculations upon which the

---

* The word surveyor is used to represent the builder's quantity surveyor as opposed to the quantity surveyor employed by the client.

estimate is based are properly recorded to establish records for future projects and provide vital information to the surveyor, buyer, planner, contracts manager and bonus surveyor should the tender be successful.

Surveyor

The builder's (quantity) surveyor is responsible for financial and contractual matters. His involvement commences at the tendering stage by assisting the estimator with the documents received. He may also provide cost information obtained from previous projects where relevant to the current estimate. Points of interest must be reported to management for consideration when preparing the tender. A likely cash flow is also produced to aid this process.

During the building period the surveyor is responsible for measuring and valuing the progress of the works, including variations, in order to monitor the cash flow and check the valuations and final account prepared by the quantity surveyor. An important part of this work involves checking that the measurements inserted in the bill of quantities correspond with those of the finished work carried out in accordance with the architect's drawings. He also provides any information necessary to enable the quantity surveyor to carry out his duties.

The surveyor normally liaises with the quantity surveyor on matters concerning the builder's account and may negotiate with him in respect to the valuation of the works, especially in relation to contractual claims and the like. Issues arising from sub-contractor's accounts, especially those of nominated sub-contractors, are brought to the attention of the quantity surveyor on their behalf unless the issue is one which is unrelated to the main contract.

The surveyor may be responsible for measuring and valuing the weekly earnings of the builder's site operatives such as joiners, bricklayers and labourers. Earnings of these operatives are usually linked to some form of incentive scheme. Bonus schemes and the like generally work on the basis that the operative is paid additional monies for all output exceeding that which is equivalent to his basic guaranteed pay. In many firms the task is performed by a cost and bonus surveyor or officer. The cost and bonus surveyor must provide the site agent and surveyor with details of labour costs for cost control purposes.

Buyer

The builder's buyer is responsible for obtaining quotations from suppliers and sub-contractors and the scheduling and placing of orders to meet site production requirements. This also entails entering negotiations with these respective organisations to obtain the lowest possible prices.

Many builders operate a system whereby the value of quotations is reduced at tender and, if successful in winning the contract, then either negotiate a lower price, an increased discount or obtain a more competitive quotation from another organisation. This is not considered by the author to be good practice as organisations providing quotations may submit prices that are not competitive in the knowledge that there will be an opportunity to give a competitive price at a later date. When organisations are constantly placed in this situation there is no reason to believe that they do not play the same game as the builder by adding a percentage to their quotation in order to take it off later. In situations where work is abundant, reputable organisations may be more reluctant to accept such practices, thus increasing the builder's risk.

Planner

The builder's planner is responsible for selecting the most cost and time effective method of carrying out the work, programming each activity of work in a co-ordinated order so as to provide continuity of work primary for the builder's operations, establishing labour and plant requirements, providing details of site requirements such as staffing, hutting, access and the proposed layout of the site.

Duties start during the tendering period when the planner liaises with the contracts manager, and subsequently the estimator, on the method of construction and resources to be used. The initial programme and methods prepared at this stage are compared with the estimator's data to ensure that all calculations correspond. The programme is used by management when preparing the tender and may be used by the surveyor or the planner in conjunction with the contracts manager to establish the pre-tender cash flow.

Once the contract is awarded to the builder the planner is initially responsible for preparing the main construction programme, copies of which will be supplied to the architect, quantity surveyor if required, the contracts manager and site agent. This programme is used to prepare detailed cash flows and to monitor site progress. The planner, in liaison with site management, is also responsible for carrying out all necessary programme and other related revisions to maintain site output.

Contracts manager

The builder's contracts manager is responsible for ensuring that the sites under his control are managed efficiently and economically.[4] His involvement starts at the tendering stage with advice to the estimator on matters relating to construction workload, availability of labour and the like.

During the building period the manager supervises the work of the site agents and liaises with other members of the builder's organisation involved with his sites along with the architects in order that production proceeds on or ahead of programme. Any construction problems must therefore be overcome in advance of the work on site commencing.[5]

The contracts manager in liaison with the site agent and foreman may deviate from the initial plan of work to save time or increase profit margins. This requires close control of production programmes, site costs and productivity.

Site agent

The builder's site agent is responsible for the everyday planning and running of the site efficiently and economically. This involves controlling any foremen, maintaining an adequate workforce on site, ensuring that plant and materials are available when required and co-ordinating the work of sub-contractors. In addition he is also responsible for ensuring that all safety and other regulations are complied with.

At various times he provides the contracts manager with reports on progress and expenditure and submits productivity data to the estimator. He may also liaise with the client's representatives and deal with visitors to the site. Correspondence in writing may be delegated to the site agent by the contracts manager although this depends both on the nature of the business concerned and the typing facilities on site.

To enable the site agent to carry out his work effectively it is the responsibility of the foreman to assist in the planning of the work and act as link between the management and the workforce. On small projects it may only be necessary to employ a foreman rather than a site agent.

Others employed by the builder

Depending on the size of the firm the builder may also employ others with the sole responsibility for such functions as safety, plant management and personnel. Where the firm is too small to employ such additional specialists these tasks must be allocated to those within the organisation.

Planning officer

The planning officer is employed by the local authority and is responsible for the specialist officers, within his department, who performs the various tasks.

One aspect of the work undertaken is that of vetting planning applications to ensure that they comply with the various Town and

Country Planning Acts and other government legislation. The main responsibility in this respect is to regulate land and property development in a manner which is not detrimental to the local environment.

Approval or rejection is determined by committee although this is usually delegated to an individual in the case of simple applications such as the construction of a single dwelling in a residental area.[6] Planning approval must be obtained prior to commencement of the building work although the local authority levies a fee for this service.

District surveyor

The district surveyor or building control officer is employed by the local authority to ensure that building work is carried out in accordance with the prevailing government legislation and local controls or regulations introduced by individual local authorities.

Prior to commencing work on site appropriately details of the proposed building work must be submitted to the district surveyor along with the correct fee. The plans and other documents are then checked and if they comply with the Building Regulations of that area they are passed for approval. This requirement applies to new buildings, building extensions, the provision of services and fittings plus any alterations to buildings which could affect structural stability or create a fire hazard or interfere with occupants escaping from the building.[7] If approval is not given due to non-compliance with any regulation then amendments must be made to the submission by the architect or others responsible for obtaining approval.

The district surveyor is also responsible for checking the progress of the work on site at specific stages and times when deemed appropriate to ensure that the Building Regulations are adhered to by the builder in accordance with the approved plans. The builder is responsible for issuing such notices of inspection to the district surveyor, starting with the notice that work has commenced. Where work is found not to conform with the Building Regulations the district surveyor has the authority to instruct the builder to remedy the work. Where the builder does not act on such instructions the district surveyor may arrange for the remedial work to be carried out by others, the cost of which is claimed from the builder.

Health and safety inspector

The health and safety inspector is employed by the health and safety law enforcement agency to ensure that regulations and codes of practice relating to the Health and Safety at Work Act 1974 are observed on building sites. Prior to this Act the work was performed by the factory inspector in accordance with the Factories Act 1961.[8]

His responsibility is to check that standards are maintained for the protection of those on the site and has the power to prosecute any builder that defaults. The health and safety officer has the authority to inspect any aspect of the site which may be detrimental to working conditions including the taking of samples of materials for analysis. Inspections of the site for safety include excavations, hoisting, scaffold and protection from moving parts on machinery; those for health include washing, drying, mess room, toilet and first-aid facilities.

When working with dangerous or toxic materials the regulations covering such materials must be followed at all times. The builder must also give prior notice to the health and safety officer, where possible, of any intention to work with these materials.

Project organisation   There are a number of ways in which a building project may be organised although they all possess similar characteristics. In this respect there is a client, a designer with his associates and a builder with his associates. These parties loosely constitute a group commonly referred to as the building team for the project.[9] In some cases the builder is the designer, although this arrangement is discussed later.

The method of organising a project is shown in figure 2.1 which identifies the relevant parties and the functions they perform.

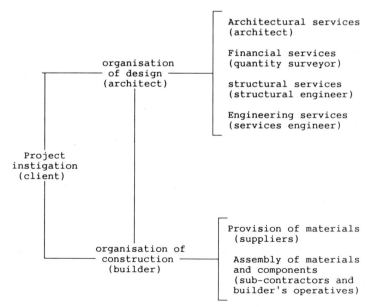

Figure 2.1   Organisational structure of a project

Contractual arrangements

Transfer of risk   In order to engage a building contractor it is first necessary to establish the terms of the engagement. This requires the selection of an appropriate method of determining the amount payable to the builder prior to the commencement of the work and also the means of assessing any additional payments during the building period so that the final amount may be established on completion of the work. In addition, the agreed relationships and responsibilities of the client and builder must be decided.

The combination of these two aspects constitute the legally binding (or contractual) arrangements for a project. The contractual arrangements selected influence the level of risk taken by the client and the building contractor. By varying the arrangements the risk may be transferred from one to the other.

The amount payable to the builder   Contracts fall into the category of either fixed price* or cost reimbursement. In addition, fixed price contracts may be firm or fluctuating.

A fixed price contract exists when the amount payable is agreed prior to work commencing on site. On domestic work this is often straightforward, for example a quotation for installing double glazing represents the amount payable on completion. If the quotation for double glazing is expressed as a cost per square metre this also constitutes a fixed price contract as the amount payable will be based on a price already agreed irrespective of its actual cost to the builder. However, in almost all other circumstances where the work is of a more complex nature the amount payable will differ from the initial price agreed. This is because variations in the work occur after the initial agreement.

A cost reimbursement contract exists when the amount payable is not agreed prior to work commencing on site. In this situation the amount payable is the net (prime) cost incurred by the builder for labour, materials and plant plus a sum of money to cover for overheads and profit (fee). On domestic work for example, a quotation for installing double glazing would merely state that the amount payable on completion of the work will be based on the prime cost plus a fee.

The amount payable on completion is therefore unknown

---

* The term 'fixed price' must not be confused with the term 'firm price'. Firm price is an entirely different concept relating to a specific contract condition. Briefly the condition, which is optional to the client prior to tender, requires the builder to include in his tender for all allowances considered necessary to cover for future fluctuations in costs. Where fluctuations are incorporated into the contract the builder does not include for future fluctuations in his tender. Here the client is liable for reimbursing the builder for such costs in accordance with the contract conditions.

although an indication of the final cost may be provided. Where work is of a more complex nature an approximate estimate is prepared and used as a basis upon which the builder determines the level of fee required. In this situation the builder is informed of the method by which the fee is to be determined.

With a fixed price contract the risk to the client is reduced as his financial commitment relating to building work is to a great extent determined in advance. It is the builder who takes the risk of being able to carry out the work at a profit. The risk is further transferred to the builder in circumstances where a firm price is given.

A cost reimbursement contract has the reverse effect as risk remains with the client, the extent of which is influenced both by the fee method selected and the degree of cost control carried out by the client's representative.

The decision as to which is most suitable depends on the particular circumstances relating to each project. In some cases it is better to select cost reimbursement rather than fixed price. Take for example a client whose factory building has just suffered extensive fire damage causing production to be suspended. If the client is desperate to resume production immediately and is prepared to pay any likely shortfalls in cash from his insurance company then a logical solution is a cost reimbursement contract. This allows a quick start on site as extensive documents do not have to be produced in order to obtain a competitive tender.

Arrangements for determining the amount payable   There are a number of ways in which to determine both fixed price and cost reimbursement. Some of the alternative arrangements have further risk implications for the client and the builder. These alternatives are as follows:

Fixed price based on:

Specification and drawings

The builder's price is submitted as a lump sum (single figure). The builder must establish the extent of the work to be undertaken by measuring the quantities from the drawings and on site where necessary. The builder's risk is therefore greater than where bills of quantities or schedules are used. The drawings provide graphical representation of the work, including dimensions and possibly specification notes. The specification describes the work to be carried out and the materials to be used. Alternatives to the traditional specification include a performance* specification and a quantified specification.

Schedule of rates

The builder's price is submitted as a series of unit rates, say £60 per cubic metre for concrete or £16 per square metre for brickwork, inserted by the builder against each work item on the schedule. The work is measured on completion to determine the amount payable to the builder. Alternatively, schedules such as those produced by the PSA require the builder to insert a percentage addition or omission against a pre-priced schedule, the prices in the PSA schedule being updated every ten years or so. Suitable for maintenance and repair work or when there is no time available to prepare more detailed information or when the amount of work to be carried out has not been established.

Bill of approximate quantities

The builder's price is submitted as a lump sum (single figure) based on the totals of the amounts for each work item. Each item amount is calculated by multiplying the unit rate, inserted by the builder, by the quantity provided. The work is re-measured on completion to determine the amount payable to the builder. Suitable for use where the work cannot be defined in detail before commencement and when there is no time available to prepare more detailed information.

Bill of quantities

The builder's price is submitted as a lump sum in the same way as that for the bill of approximate quantities. However, as the quantities are firm the work is not remeasured and the amount payable is the lump sum which may be adjusted due to variations, incorrect quantities and the like. Some sections of the bill may be in the form of approximate (provisional) quantities. These sections relate to work that cannot be determined in detail at the time of the bill preparation such as builder's work in connection with nominated sub-contractors' work, ground works and drainage. Provisional quantities are subject to re-measurement on completion in order to ascertain the amount payable to the builder.

---

* This contains details of what is required and the builder decides how this is to be achieved. An example of this is where the requirement is to install a small bore heating system to meet specific requirements. Here the builder is responsible for selecting a suitable type and size of boiler and means of distributing heat to achieve this, thus further increasing his risk.

Cost reimbursement based on:

Prime cost plus percentage fee

The builder's price is the prime cost estimated by the client plus a percentage stated by the builder. The amount payable to the builder is the prime cost incurred plus the percentage addition. This arrangement provides the builder with no incentive to be cost and time effective. Inflating the costs artificially in order to be paid more is a possibility in this situation but should not take place when dealing with reputable builders.

Prime cost plus fixed fee

The builder's price is the estimated prime cost plus a fixed amount of money added on by the builder. The amount payable to the builder is the prime cost incurred in carrying out the work plus the fixed amount. This arrangement provides the builder with a little incentive to be cost and time effective in that the fee expressed as a percentage is inversely proportional to the prime cost incurred. Thus, given that the estimated prime cost is £100,000, a fixed fee of £30,000 represents 30% mark-up. If the actual prime cost is £120,000 then, whilst the builder receives the £30,000 fee, the mark-up achieved is only 25%.

Prime cost plus fluctuating fee

This is similar to fixed fee but requires the builder to quote alternative fixed amounts against a series of estimated prime cost ranges. Typical ranges could be £80,000–90,000, £90,000–100,000, and so on. The amount payable to the builder is the actual prime cost plus the fixed amount for the range applicable.

Prime cost plus target fee

This is a more complicated arrangement whereby a target cost is initially agreed. In order to establish the target the builder prices an approximate bill of quantities, indicating the proportion of overheads and profit. The bill total, less the overheads and profit, becomes the target. The actual prime cost is monitored during the building period to determine actual cost. The difference in cost between the target and the actual cost is shared between the client and the builder. If actual cost exceeds target then both absorb the loss. If target exceeds actual cost then both share the gain.

There is therefore a great incentive for the builder to be cost and time effective as he retains a share of any cost savings. It must also be remembered that the builder is also sharing a proportion of the risk. Unlike a fixed price contract with cost reimbursement the client has a very keen interest in the costs incurred by the builder.

An example of the way in which the system operates is shown as follows:

Target cost with 50:50 share	£85,000	
Overheads and profit	£15,000	

	A	**B**
Actual cost	£95,000	£77,000
Revised total	£110,000	£92,000
Amount paid to builder	£105,000	£96,000

In this example where the target is exceeded (**A**) the builder receives £10,000 more than actual cost to cover overheads and profit as opposed to £19,000 when less than the target (**B**). If actual cost equals target then the amount will be the original £15,000.

In a more realistic situation the volume of work would differ from that set out in the bill due to variations. This is taken into account by adjusting the target in accordance with such variations so as not to distort the assessment of the builders performance. Thus, if in the above example the actual cost of £95,000 is inclusive of £20,000 additional work then the amount paid to the builder is £115,000.

Tendering arrangements

Once the contractual arrangements have been completed then suitable tendering arrangements can be selected. Tendering arrangements are concerned with the way in which a price is obtained from the builder. This may involve either competitive or non-competitive tendering.

Competitive tendering This is where a number of builders compete against each other to establish the most favourable bid. The competitive element is usually the price submitted but may also include the contract duration. Some clients may be prepared to accept a higher price in order to have the work completed in a shorter time than that offered by the other tenderers. Where the duration of the building (contract) period is stipulated by the client the price is the competitive element although many builders attempt to gain an unfair advantage over their competitors by offering two tenders. The first is a price based on the contract period and the second an alternative price based on a reduced contract period.

There are two ways of obtaining a competitive tender, these being either *open* or *selective tendering*.

Open tendering is where an invitation to tender for a project is publicised in the local and national press for any interested builder wishing to submit a tender. Tender documents are issued upon payment of a deposit, this being refundable to all builders on submission of a tender. Where the method of tendering is based on a bill of quantities the builder is required to submit a fully priced bill in addition to the tender form. The number of builders allowed to tender is unrestricted and may involve as many as sixty, thus the chances of being successful are low. Further, the practical and financial ability of such tenderers may be·ignored, resulting in unfair competition for reputable builders and a high level of risk for the client. However, the method usually results in a very low tender being obtained.

Selective tendering is where the number of builders that are to be allowed to tender are restricted. Those tendering are preselected based on their reputation and ability to carry out the work in question and their interest in submitting a competitive tender.

Non-competitive tendering   In this situation a single builder is selected to submit a price. Where this involves negotiation the builder and the client work together in order to reach an agreement as to the basis upon which the amount payable to the builder is to be determined. The manner in which the negotiations are conducted depends on the extent to which the client needs to know his cost commitment and the urgency to complete the work. Negotiation is usually selected when the client prefers one particular builder to carry out the work, either for personal reasons or due to past performance.

Tendering procedures to obtain a competitive price   This refers to the activities that are performed in order to obtain tenders. There are two methods available, these being *single stage* and *two stage tendering*. The concept of *single stage tendering* is that the builder submits a tender based on the documents provided and if accepted the contract is made.

With *two stage tendering* the contract is not made as a result of a successful tender. The *first stage*, this being a tender based on provisional information, is a selection process both to determine the most favourable builder and to establish a competitive pricing mechanism. The *second stage* involves the builder contributing to the development of the project. The contract is then based on a revised price which is calculated by applying the tender pricing to the final design details.

In some two stage tendering situations, such as those for design and build or joint venture, each builder is interviewed by the client during the second stage. Whilst traditionally two stage tendering is not as common as single stage tendering this is changing with the increasing popularity of the alternative procurement routes which to a varying degree provide greater opportunities for builders to contribute to project design and management.

Code of procedure for single stage tendering   The National Joint Consultative Committee for Building in collaboration with other bodies have produced a code of procedure for single stage selective tendering (1989) and also for two stage selective tendering (1983). The two documents outline the recommended procedure to be followed by those who commission building work.

A synopsis of the code of procedure for single stage tendering 1989, with reference to the respective clauses, is as follows:

2.2   The code assumes the use of standard forms of building contract.

2.3   Builder's tender is the price for which he offers to carry out and complete the work shown on the drawings and described in the bill of quantities and/or specification.

2.4   Tendered price should not be altered without justification except for errors found before acceptance, these being dealt with in accordance with clause 6.

3.1   Numbers of builders to be asked to submit a tender:

Size of contract	Maximum number of tenderers
up to £50,000	5
£50,000 to £250,000	6
£250,000 to £1 million	8
Over £1 million	6

3.2   Guidelines for selecting short list of tenderers.

3.4   Object of selection is to restrict final choice to the firm offering the lowest tender.

4.1   Preliminary enquiry to establish which contractors are willing to submit tenders, dispatch of tender documents to be within a suggested period of four to six weeks.

4.2   Details of tender documents.

4.3 Time allowed for tendering being a minimum of four working weeks in order that competitive quotations for material supply and sub-contract work can be obtained.

4.4 Tenders should all be based upon identical documents and not qualified by any tenderer.

4.5 Under English law any tender may with withdrawn before its acceptance.

5.1 Tenders to be opened as soon as possible after time for receipt.

5.2 Lowest tenderer asked to submit a priced bill of quantities.

5.3 All but the three lowest tenderers should be informed immediately that they have been unsuccessful. The second and third lowest are informed that they were not the most favourable but may be approached again.

5.4 Once the contract is let then all tenderers should be supplied with a list of tender prices.

6.1 Priced bill to be examined by the quantity surveyor.

6.2 Object of examination is to detect errors in computation of tender. Where errors are found they are dealt with by one of two alternatives. The decision as to which alternative is to be used must be made before tenders are requested and tenderers informed.

6.3 Alternative 1: tenderer given option of confirming tender or withdrawing. If withdraws then the second lowest tenderer is approached in a similar way.

6.3.2 If tender confirmed then the bill is endorsed to say that all rates or prices, excluding preliminary items, contingencies PC and provisional sums, are to be reduced or increased in the same proportion as the corrected total of priced items exceeds or falls short of such items. Endorsement to be signed by both parties.

6.4 Alternative 2: tenderer given opportunity of confirming offer or amending it to correct errors. If amended and offer now no longer the lowest then second lowest approached.

6.4.2 If not amended, but confirmed, then endorsement as 6.3.2 required.

6.5 When tender found to be free from error or tenderer agrees to stand by it then the employer should be recommended to accept.

7.1 Should tender exceed employer's budget then price to be negotiated with the lowest tenderer. If negotiations fail then approach second lowest.

Procurement systems

Procurement is a term used to describe the manner in which a client commissions building work. Procurement systems are basically global terms which categorise the alternative methods of managing a project, brought about by the increase in the number of non-traditional approaches practised in the United Kingdom.[10] With some methods the concept is partly a combination of both contractual and tendering arrangements/procedures. Codes of procedure published by the NJCC for two alternatives include the code of procedure for selective tendering for design and build (1985) and joint venture tendering for construction in the UK, guidance note 1 (1985).

Before proceeding further it is worth mentioning one aspect often neglected in design development relating the contribution made by specialist sub-contractors. Such organisations can play a vital role by offering unique expertise to the design process. This is especially so where their work either forms a significant part of the project or is critical in respect of integration with the phasing and execution of the builder's work. Due to the number of problems associated with specialist installations which occur both during and after construction there is certainly scope for improvement. Benefits would be achieved by reducing this source of time and cost escalation although more important to the client would be the bliss of occupying a building in which all the services function properly.

Traditional procurement   The building industry has evolved over many hundreds of years. During this time there have been many developments such as the introduction of bills of quantities and a standard method of measurement to govern their production. Further, many procedures have been established including those for procurement. For many years the method of procurement was for a client to employ an architect, responsible for managing the project along with providing the design, and a builder, responsible for carrying out the construction work (and maybe a limited amount of design). This method still remains popular.

In addition to the basic fixed price and cost reimbursement arrangements within traditional procurement there are a number of unique variations such as joint venture, serial, continuation and term:

Joint venture

This is where the builder joins forces with a services contractor, thus forming a consortium, to tender for work. The parties to the consortium are equally responsible for their own work and that of the other irrespective of whether either party defaults. Contacts are awarded on the basis of the tender submitted and an interview to determine the extent to which the services are integrated with the builder's work. Such contracts are used for hospitals and other like projects where the services account for a large proportion of the total work.

Alternatively joint venture may refer to a consortium in context with development. Here the builder joins forces with local or central government to finance and build, as in the case of the London Dockland Developments, Thames Flood Barrier, Channel Tunnel and other initiatives.

Serial contracting

This is where the builder tenders for a project in the knowledge that subject to satisfactory performance a given number of similar projects will automatically be awarded. The first contract is obtained by competitive tender and subsequent contracts are negotiated on the basis of the first. As part of the negotiation process consideration is given to any fluctuations in cost that may have occurred since the time of the initial tender. This arrangement provides a learning curve for the builder which should with each subsequent project lead to increased time and cost savings for the client. In addition, the arrangement acts as an incentive for builders to be highly competitive. Serial contracting is suitable where a number of similar projects are to be completed over a period of time: local authority programmes for replacing existing infant schools being a typical example.

Continuation contracting

This is similar to serial contracting with the builder being offered further work of a comparable nature as a result of excellent performance. The major difference here is that at tender stage the likelihood of further work does not exist. In the absence of such a carrot the tenders are likely to be less competitive than with serial contracting although subsequent benefits should be similar.

Term contract

This is an arrangement whereby the builder agrees to carry out work intermittently during a set period, say one year or eighteen months, for a fixed price. The builder tenders on a schedule of rates without the knowledge of how much work is required. To add to the builder's pricing problems he has no knowledge of when the work is to be carried out. The tender is normally required to be on a firm price basis. All the abortive travelling time and lost hours due to part day workloads have to be allowed for in the individual rates along with overheads and profit.

Once the contract is awarded the builder must carry out work at such times as the client gives written notice thereof. Thus, if the work involves repairs to a housing estate, the builder may receive notice to replace chimney pots to three houses and replace one length of guttering to two properties. Having completed the work the builder may after four weeks receive notice to replace chimney pots to another three properties, and so on until the end of the contracted term. The builder is paid for the number of items carried out at the rates contained in the schedule. Term contracts are suitable for maintenance work where the amount of work to be carried out is undecided.

Non-traditional procurement Alternative methods of procurement are now available to clients and whilst they are presently not as popular there are indications that preference over traditional procurement[11] is increasing. These alternatives are[12] design and build, management contracting, project management and the BPF system:

Design and build

This differs from traditional procurement because here the client employs a builder to be responsible for both the management and execution of design and building work. All the risk is therefore transferred to the builder.

The builder may use in-house architects or commission a local practice to deal with the design aspects. The advantage to the builder is that full control of the design is retained, thus, features which are impractical or awkward to carry out on site can be rejected. The builder is awarded the contract on the basis of price, design and speed of completion, and selection usually includes an interview with the client. The builder's package may be obtained through negotiation or in competition with payment based on fixed price or occasionally cost reimbursement.

The client may employ at any time separate consultants, such as an architect or quantity surveyor to provide advice on the various issues. Originally used to providing less complex buildings or even standard systems for clients that are not likely to require constant amendments to an agreed design. However, this is fast changing as larger and more complex projects incorporate design and build.

One variation to the concept is develop and construct. The builder bids on the basis of outline drawings and performance specification provided by the client. The successful builder is then responsible for developing the initial design and the subsequent building work.

Another variation is turnkey. This expression, which originated from the USA, evolved from the fact that the builder provided the client with a fully designed building, including all the necessary plant and equipment for immediate use, all the client did was turn the key.

Project management

This differs from other methods of procurement because here the client employs a consultant with professional and commercial responsibilities to manage the whole building process from inception to completion, operating within a set budget. The criteria for appointing a project manager include the size and type of fee and site overheads required plus the level of expertise offered. Usually the fee is adjustable so as to reflect the performance of the manager. The budget is a form of target, derived by approximate estimating techniques, which can be used to measure management performance. To secure the best possible terms of appointment the client may approach more than one manager.

Whilst the appointed manager is responsible for managing the building team's activities each member of the team signs a separate contract of employment with the client. The building work may either be contracted out to one builder (traditional or design and build arrangement) or split into unique work packages for separate letting (management contracting arrangement). This system is suitable for large projects where the extra cost incurred by employing a manager is outweighed by the accrued benefits and where the client wishes to retain full control of the process. As the cost of building work is not fixed at the outset the financial risk remains with the client.

Management contracting

Not to be confused with project management,[13] this differs from other methods of procurement in that the client employs a builder to manage the building work, under the direction of a project administrator or manager. Management contracting however may take alternative forms, one of which being that the builder may also be required to carry out the building work, although this is not contemplated with the JCT form of management contract. The manager is paid a fee based on an estimated target cost of the building work plus site support costs and the prime costs incurred in employing firms to carry out the building work.

Where the management contractor is not required to carry out the building work it is split into unique packages and separate sub-contractors are engaged to complete each package, usually on a firm fixed price basis. This system allows the design of each package to be completed whilst building work continues on site for the earlier designed packages. The possible benefits resulting from this are: reduction of overall project period; design may take into account of construction problems on site; late variations may be incorporated into the design; more favourable tenders may be obtained with each work package. Suitable for large complex projects. The financial risk remains with the client.

The BPF system

The BPF system was developed for the British Property Federation as an alternative to other contracting methods as such alternatives were considered inefficient and detrimental to the interest of the client.[14] It is a system which fosters an attitude of co-operation between the members of the building team and requires of each member a high level of responsibility. This is achieved by setting time and cost targets for all members (not just the builder), incorporating penalties for non-performance and introducing an element of shared responsibility. Reference to the BPF manual is recommended to appreciate the full implications of the system.

All members of the building team except the builder have non-traditional titles. Details of the duties and responsibilities of each member are set out in detail.

Consultants are paid a fixed fee, rather than a percentage of the project value, with adjustments for effective performance. However, design must be carried out within a stipulated time and completed before the tendering period. Note that the builder is required to design any part of the work which is incomplete and therefore design costs must be incorporated within the builder's tender sum. All design details produced by the builder must be approved by the client's representative.

The tender submission consists of documents prepared by the builder, these being an outline priced schedule of activities, an organisational chart, details of personnel, method statement, a list of declared sub-contractors and a schedule of time charges. The client may prefer to use bills of quantities in which case whilst a priced schedule is not required an unpriced works programme similar to a schedule of activities is required. However, their inclusion will increase design fees and extend the design period. Note that builders may submit alternative proposals.

The priced schedule of activities incorporates design,

management and building activities for which the builder is responsible. The priced schedule also includes a programme of such activities and the resources to be employed together with details of the method of construction to be adopted. Prior to signing the main contract the successful bidder is normally asked to provide a more detailed schedule of activities. This developed schedule then supersedes the outline schedule submitted at tender.

The format in which the schedule is prepared and the level of detail contained therein is important to the builder as it is the basis of determining the stages of payment. Each activity shown on the schedule should represent the completed stages of the work for which payment is required. Thus, in addition to his own work the builder must also obtain the stages of payment required by each sub-contractor. The client may prefer to use bills of quantities in which case a priced schedule is not required. Whilst the BPF manual recommends that firm price tenders are obtained this may be inappropriate for projects of long duration, especially as the system has been specifically written for use with medium sized projects. Thus, for contracts exceeding two years duration fluctuations are incorporated into the contract. Fluctuations in costs are adjusted on the basis of a single index and only 80% of the value of each activity is subject to adjustment. The builder must therefore anticipate any shortfalls in recovery of increased costs associated with this method and include such sums in the tender sum.

The tender documents issued to builders for competitive tendering consist of the invitation to tender, the complete drawings, specifications with possible sections relating to building services on a performance basis, conditions of contract and in addition a bill of quantities should the client prefer. For certain specialist work the client may obtain designs and prices from a number of sub-contractors. The names of these organisations together with their respective quotations may be issued to builders to assist the bidding process. As naming is not contemplated the builder is free to approach other sub-contractors if he so wishes. Thus, maximum flexibility is maintained within the system of procurement. The system is suitable for projects irrespective of size or complexity. The risks associated with projects incorporating this system are very much reduced, especially for the client.

Forms of contract

Having decided upon the contractual arrangements it is then possible to select the most appropriate form of contract for the project.

Basis of a contract   A legally binding contract between parties is based on and is subsequent to an unqualified acceptance of an offer made by the other party. Building contracts are usually in writing and due to the complexity of the building process they take the form of a detailed formal document. Such formal documents contain the conditions upon which the parties to the contract are bound along with details of the procedures that must be adhered to by or in connection with others referred therein.

Different forms of contract are used throughout the world, some of which are based on English forms. One English form of contract which is in constant use on overseas projects or often provides the contract basis is the FIDIC. In England the construction industry uses forms of contract which generally suit the size and type of work to be undertaken and the type of client concerned. As a result there are a number of standard and non-standard forms in use.

Standard forms of contract   Standard forms of contract are produced for both the building and civil engineering sectors by appointed working groups that represent the respective professional institutions, industry federations and other associated bodies with a vested interest. This standardisation provides familiarity for all concerned irrespective of which part of the country they are from. Separate forms are used for the main contract between client and builder and for the supplementary contracts between the builder and sub-contractors, whether nominated or not.

The advantage of using sets of forms produced by one particular working group is that the sub-contracts are linked to the main contract, thus the interests of all concerned within a project are to an extent maintained. Whilst in principle the standard forms contain common conditions there is provision for variation as some clauses, such as those for insurance of the works, allow the client to choose one option from a number of alternatives. Also specific conditions relating to individual projects are required to be inserted in the appendix to the document. Standard conditions which are not the subject of either alternative selection or data insertion are intended to be used unamended. However, consultants and builders do amend conditions contained in both main contracts and sub-contracts. This is usually intended to impose onerous conditions on the receiving party. Not only is this considered bad practice such action may backfire, resulting in adverse contractual implications for those that have made the amendments.[15]

Whilst some seek to amend contract clauses others attempt to introduce new clauses such as the highly controversial Brown Clause of the early eighties.[16] This clause required builders to include in there tenders a sum for loss and expense that may be incurred at some future date. As the sum was to form part of the competitive price the amount included by the builder had to be unrealistically low to maintain their competitiveness. Some builders may have no alternative other than to accept unfair conditions in order to obtain work. However, such acceptance by builders is no justification for their implementation.

Building contracts in Scotland relate to Scottish law and differ from those used in England. The various standard forms of main contract used for building in England and Wales are under constant review.

A list of current documents is as follows although it must be noted that new forms may have since been introduced and some may already be superseded by later revisions.

Standard building contracts issued by the Joint Contracts Tribunal (JCT):

Private editions	*Local authority editions*	
JCT 80: with Quantities without Quantities with approximate Quantities	JCT 80: with Quantities without Quantities with approximate Quantities	
IFC 84: with Quantities without Quantities	for simple works although many consultants use this on large projects in preference to JCT 80	
Agreement for Minor Building Works, 1980		
Agreement for Renovation Grant Works, 1975	an alternative to MBW 80	
Fixed Fee Form of Prime Cost Contract, 1967 revised		
With Contractor's Design, 1981	used on Design and Build contracts	
Contractor's Design portion Supplement, 1981	used with JCT 80 with Quantities when the builder is responsible for designing part of the work	
Management Contract, 1987	main contract between the client and management contractor (MC). Sub-contract between the MC and the works contractors (WC) is Works Contract/2 with WC/1 tendering documents. There is also an employer/works contractor agreement.	

Standard forms of sub-contract for use with JCT 80 are as follows:

NSC/4   Nominated sub-contract for use with NSC/1*
NSC/4a   Nominated sub-contract for use when NSC/1 is not used
NSC/2   Agreement between the client (employer) and the nominated sub-contractor for use with NSC/1
NSC/2a   Employer/Sub-contractor Agreement for use when NSC/1 is not used
DOM/1   Domestic sub-contractors under the JCT 80 contract
NAM/SC   Named sub-contractors under the Intermediate Form of Building Contract (IFC 84)
ESA/1#   Employer/Sub-contractor Agreement for named sub-contractors under the IFC 84 contract

Contracts other than those issued by the JCT are also in use. Some of these forms are as follows:

Form GC/Works/1, 1977	main contract issued by the Property Services Agency (PSA) for use on central government projects for either building or civil engineering work. The form of sub-contract available is GW/S
Form GC/Works/2, 1980	main contract used on central government projects for minor works, normally below £50,000 in value
ACA Form of Building Agreement, 1982	main contract for use with or without Quantities and issued by the Association of Consultant Architects. The 1982 form of sub-contract is available
ACA Form of Building Agreement 1984 (BPF edition)	main contract for the BPF system and issued by the British Properties Federation[17]
FAS Building Contract	main contract issued by the Faculty of Architects and Surveyors for use on work of a simple nature
NFBTE Design and Build, 1974	main contract

---

* NSC/1 is a standard sub-contract tender form. If this form is not used to obtain such tenders then the employer and the architect are committed to using the *a* version of NSC documents. Where NSC/1 is used the architect must also nominate a sub-contractor using an NSC/3 form.

This is issued by the RIBA and may accompany the Tender and Agreement NAM/T issued by the JCT.

| ICE Conditions of contract | main contract issued by the institution of civil engineers for use on civil engineering projects |
| ICE Conditions of contract for Minor Works 1988 | main contract for use on projects of short duration and not exceeding £100,000 in value. The form of sub-contract issued by the Federation of Civil Engineering Contractors is also available. |

Each form of main contract and sub-contract issued by the JCT has a separate contract document which deals with the contractor's cost fluctuations. The JCT also issue Practice Note documents to aid implementation of the contract documents.

Prior to JCT 80 the official form of building contract in use was the Standard Form of Building Contract 1963 edition (July 1972 Revision) issued by the JCT. Although not recommended for current use there is evidence that contracts are still being let on JCT 63.[18] This document has therefore proved very popular with consultants and consequently it will be some time before it is phased out in practice. Perhaps the reason for the unpopularity of JCT 80 has something to do with the fact that it contains far more occasions when the architect is required to take action, as opposed to allowing such action to be optional, than does JCT 63. This is brought about by the increased use of the word *shall* in lieu of *may*.

There are other forms of contract which are produced by bodies such as the regional health authorities. These forms are used exclusively by the bodies that produce them and in this respect they are referred to as non-standard forms of contract.[19]

Non-standard forms of contract are also written by contractors, quantity surveyors, local authorities and private clients. Because standard forms of contract are not always available to suit the growing number of procurement systems it is inevitable that non-standard forms are produced.

Contract documents

There are a number of documents that can be used as a contract document. They constitute contract documents in that they contain the terms and conditions of the agreement plus specific details relating to the work to be carried out. A combination of documents are used as appropriate although each must be signed by both parties to the contract. Two sets of documents are provided for this purpose to enable each party to retain one copy.

Documents commonly used as contract documents for building work are as follows:

form of contract – containing the articles of agreement, the general conditions and the appendix

contract drawings – design drawings upon which the contract sum included in the form of contract is based

bill of quantities (either firm or approximate) – document containing preliminaries, preambles, measured work, prime cost and provisional sums, tender summary and a copy of the form of tender

specification – used in lieu of, although similar in content to, certain sections of a bill of quantities except that there are no quantities

schedule of rates – description of each work item without quantities which may require the builder to insert unit rates against the items. Unit rates, including preliminaries and mark-up allowances, are calculated by the builder in the normal manner. Approximate quantities are derived to assist the process to establish both the likely extent of the work and the approximate contract value. The Property Services Agency (PSA) have their own system whereby the builder must establish a single percentage addition or omission for the whole of the work and is derived by comparing his current rates with those contained in the PSAs current pre-priced Schedule of Rates for Building Works published by the Department of the Environment. Where the full extent of the work is uncertain it may be necessary to establish percentage adjustments for each item which then have to be weighted and converted into single percentages for each section which are in turn weighted and converted into the global percentage which represents the bid. Payment for each item of work done is determined by the PSAs unit rate multiplied by the quantity completed and then adjusted by the builder's bid percentage.

If for example a specification is used the accompanying documents could be a form of tender and drawings. Where a bill of quantities is used the bill replaces the specification within the group. However, it is possible for a house owner to engage a builder on nothing more than a verbal or written quotation. Also for small jobs of a more formal nature a form of contract and drawings may suffice, the drawings containing the detailed specification.

Where bills of quantities are included the Standard Method of Measurement of Building Works, issued by the Royal Institution of Chartered Surveyors (RICS), does not qualify as a contract document. However, as the bill refers to the SMM there is a direct contractual link between the two.

Some documents currently in use are peculiar to certain forms of contract especially those for design and build and the BPF system. In the case of design and build where the JCT form with contractor's design is to be used the contract documents consist of the form of contract, the employer's requirements and the contractor's proposals together with a contract sum analysis:

> The employer's requirements may identify the type, size and quality of building, approximate cost of the project and anticipated handover date.

> The contractor's proposals would include such information as price, specification, drawings, programme or contract duration and possibly a method statement which describes the way in which the work will be carried out on site. In addition, a contract sum analysis is incorporated into the contract.

> The contract sum analysis is a breakdown of the contract price and incorporates design costs during both design and construction phases. Unless a specific analysis format is specified by the client the contractor may decide for himself the level of cost detail that is to be provided. The detail may range from a simple statement containing lump sums for design costs, substructures, superstructures, internal finishes, specialist installations, external works and drainage to a fully priced bill of quantities. A popular approach is to provide an elemental breakdown of costs, based on the relevant Building Cost Information Service (BCIS) standard elements, plus design costs as identified above.

However, several JCT forms of contract make reference to a contract sum analysis. JCT have produced practice note 23 (1987) which contains a guide to the content of such an analysis to help builders prepare a sufficiently detailed breakdown of costs as this must facilitate adequate financial control at a later date.

> From the builder's point of view the level of detail to be provided is governed to an extent by the likelihood of the client changing his mind during construction. If a high proportion of variations are expected then it is advisable to give as much cost detail as possible to ensure that accurate reimbursement of such items is achieved.

> Another consideration is the arrangement for payment which may be either periodic (interim), based on value of work completed and goods on site or in stages. In the interests of both parties the financial assessment of variations requires a reasonable level of cost detail to operate properly for both parties unlike the payment arrangement which is predetermined at

tender. Here the builder states the appropriate stages of the work for which payment is required and the value of each stage. A further consideration is of course the complexity of the project. It is unlikely that the level of detail provided for a small standard factory unit will be as comprehensive as that required for projects such as those incorporating large retail and commercial units.

Where the JCT form of contract is not used the documentation and contents therein may be specified by the client although usually the builder will decide for himself. Note that in such cases the parties may agree to one lump sum payment due on completion of the works although such an arrangement is not common.

Contract documents for the BPF system consist of drawings, specification, form of contract and schedule of activities plus any other documentation specified by the client. Unlike design and build the format and contents of documentation prepared by the builder is clearly set out in the manual of the BPF system. For example, the text is supplemented by examples of priced schedules of activities and their associated developed formats. This schedule should contain all the activities necessary to complete the work such as site set-up substructure, superstructure, brickwork, roof, windows and doors, etc, as indicated in figure 2.2. Alongside each activity is inserted the relevant quantity, resources, start time in the form of week number, duration in weeks and finally price. The prices of the activities including those relating to sub-contract work are normally entered as lump sums for the purpose of tendering and then expanded by the successful bidder. The same approach is taken for presenting details of preliminary items.

Schedule of activities
for tender .....(name of project) .....(name of builder)

Activity	Quantity	Resources	Start (week)	Duration (weeks)	Price £th
1 Site set-up	*	*	1	4	30
2 Substructure	*	*	5	8	100
3 Superstructure	*	*	13	20	400
4 Brickwork	*	*	13	18	220
5 Roof	*	*	33	6	70
6 Windows/doors	*	*	30	7	65

7 ....

8 ....

Figure 2.2 Schedule of activities
Source: *The manual of the BPF system*

* Where details of quantities and resources are complex then reference is made to the developed schedule.

References

1 BUTLER, J T, *Elements of administration for building students*, third edition, Hutchinson 1982, pp 16–19.
2 WALKER, A, *Project management in construction*, Collins 1984, pp 5–7.
3 WHATLEY, G, 'Building: easing the cash burden', *Chief Executive*, February 1987, pp 37–40.
4 FRYER, B, *The practice of construction management*, Collins 1985, pp 16–29.
5 DRESSEL, G, *Organisation and management of a construction company*, Maclaren 1968, pp 127–31.
6 CULLINGWORTH, J B, *Town and country planning in Britain*, ninth edition, Allen and Unwin 1985, pp 318–21.
7 POWELL-SMITH, V, and BILLINGTON, M J, *The building regulations explained and illustrated*, seventh edition, Collins 1986, pp 25–8.
8 UFF, J, *Construction law*, fourth edition, Sweet and Maxwell 1985, pp 309–15.
9 THE AQUA GROUP, *Contract administration for architects and quantity surveyors*, sixth edition, Collins 1986, pp 1–2.
10 TURNER, D, *Design and build contract practice*, Longmans 1986, pp 4.
11 BENNETT, J, and FLANAGAN, R, 'For the good of the client', *Building*, 1 April 1983, pp 26–8.
12 BENNETT, J, and FLANAGAN, R, 'Management options', *Building*, 8 April 1983, pp 32–3.
13 MATON, P, 'Management contractor or construction manager – what is the difference?', *Building Technology and Management*, December 1987/January 1988, pp 24,27.
14 BRITISH PROPERTY FEDERATION, *Manual of the BPF system* 1983, pp 1.
15 TRIMMER, A, 'Quantifying – Amending the standard forms', *CQS*, April 1988, pp 44.
16 JENSEN, P, 'The brown clause for loss and expense', *The Quantity Surveyor*, April 1982, vol. 38, no. 4, pp 58.
17 PENNINGTON, I, 'A guide to the BPF system and contract'. *CJOB*, 1985, pp 3,8.
18 RICS, 'Junior Organisation, Survey – Contract use 1985', *CQS*, December 1986, pp 12–14.
19 TURNER, D F, *Standard contracts for building*, Godwin 1984, pp 18–24.

Questions

1 Explain how the choice of tender documents affects the financial risks borne by the client and the contractor.

2 Detailed bills of quantity have been replaced, in new procurement systems, to allow documents to be used which relate costs to operations in sufficient detail to provide efficient contract control.

Describe the likely content and evaluate the following financial control documents:

(a) Contract Sum Analysis (Design and build)
(b) Schedule of Activities (BPF System).

3 Explain the possible effects that the following trends in tendering procedures have on the preparation and adjudication of a tender:

(a) large tender lists
(b) short tender periods
(c) large contracts based on drawings and specifications.

4 Compare the documents for the financial control of TWO of the following procurement methods:

(a) Design and build
(b) Management contracting
(c) British Property Federation system.

3 Methods of Estimating

Estimates and estimating

Status of an estimate There is often confusion as to the difference between a quotation and an estimate. An *estimate* is an offer which if accepted unconditionally may be the basis of a contract, depending upon the intentions of the parties involved. This is illustrated in the precedent case Crowshaw v Pritchard (1899).[1] A *quotation* is deemed to be an offer and if unconditionally accepted is the basis of a contract.

If, for example, a builder is asked to submit an estimate for building a garage then the amount quoted is the amount to be paid by the client. The builder is seemed to be stating the amount he requires in return for carry out the work, therefore the estimate actually is a quotation or tender. However, where the builder states at the time that the estimate is an approximation of the likely charge then the amount quoted is not necessarily the amount to be paid by the client.

In a similar way, where an architect or other professional provides a client with an estimate of building costs the amount quoted is also not binding. The reason here being that the consultant is only giving an opinion as to the amount a third party is likely to charge.

Therefore further reference to estimating or estimates relates to any activity which involves the prediction of building costs, not as a substitute term for describing a quotation or tender.

Aspects of estimating Estimating is a broad term used to describe the activity of predicting building costs. Builders and consultants are both involved in such activity whilst usually attempting to achieve different goals.

The builder is mostly concerned with predicting his likely costs associated with future work that may be undertaken. The favoured way is to carry out detailed cost calculations. Here the exact cost of some items is established by obtaining quotations and prices from various sources, the data being subsequently used to price the work from first principles.

Where time does not allow detailed calculations then approximate methods may be considered. Here the builder is more likely to be predicting tender levels rather than cost due to the nature of approximate estimating data. Approximate methods may also be employed to provide early indications of project value either for use by the builder or when giving cost advice to others.

Consultants such as quantity surveyors are mostly concerned with forecasting clients' costs, this being the likely cost of building. It is in fact purely a prediction of the likely lowest tender sum as approximate estimating methods are employed. This is because the approximate estimating data used is mainly information collected from the lowest tenderers on previous jobs.

Detailed estimating similar to that carried out by builders may also be employed in situations where more realistic prediction is required by the client, where consultants prepare tenders for builders and when pricing some variations. However, in some instances it is likely that the prices of individual work items are merely transferred (with some adjustment) from priced documents submitted by lowest tenderers on previous jobs.

Estimating and tendering The tendering aspect of a builder's operations may be considered to be subservient to other activities such as site production. Nevertheless, it constitutes the life blood of the firm by providing a constant flow of work in order to achieve an acceptable level of resource utilisation. The tendering process consists of two distinctly separate activities, these being estimating and tendering:

Estimating – This is a technical process carried out by a builder in order to calculate the net costs that are likely to be incurred in carrying out specific work at a future date.

The data gathered is also important once the contract is won as it provides a useful basis for cost control, estimating feedback and financial negotiations with the client and sub-contractors which inevitably arise during the building period.

Tendering – This is a commercial function, performed by management, which involves establishing a suitable competitive tender on the basis of the net cost estimate and other information gathered during the tendering period.

Ideally, each tender should incorporate the greatest possible level of profit whilst retaining the maximum chance of success. This is hard to achieve in practice as the level of competition is uncertain.

Building costs

Cost and price It is important to understand the distinction between cost and price, which to many may seem the same. This can be explained by using the builder's tender as an example.

The tender (tender sum) consists of the builder's anticipated costs relating to labour, materials and plant plus a mark-up for profit. To the client the tender represents the *cost* of employing the builder but to the builder it represents the *price* to be paid in return for carrying out the work.

Design influence on costs   The cost effects of alternative design solutions must be considered when developing a scheme. In order to evaluate these effects it is important to appreciate how costs are influenced:

Plan shape – In theory the circle is the most economical shape as it provides the optimum wall to floor ratio (maximum floor area within a given envelope). However, the high cost of circular work together with the unusable areas that are created results in the square being more economical. Rectangular buildings have a greater perimeter (perimeter to floor ratio) than the square and therefore may also be less economical. Unfortunately the floor and roof spans of larger square buildings are likely to be of dimensions such that a costly frame is required, whereas a long narrow building of equal floor area may not have the same problem with excessive spans. Framed buildings may also require costly structural floor designs and additional column or wall supports.

Another problem associated with the square is that of internal spaces or rooms, these areas requiring artificial lighting and ventilation. Square buildings are therefore not always the most economical or practical solution. Irregular shapes are also likely to result in additional costs.

Storey height – By increasing the floor to ceiling height, and thereby increasing cubic content, costs are increased given a constant floor area. This is due to the increases in quantities for the external envelope, internal walls, increases in vertical elements of both services and wall finishes, additional heating and lighting requirements and possibly additional costs in carrying out work at greater heights.

Building height – This relates to the merits of high rise as opposed to low rise, bearing in mind that on confined sites the former may be the only viable option. Up to four storeys the cost per square metre of gross floor area is likely to reduce with height. A bungalow is therefore more expensive to build than a two storey dwelling offering the same floor area as it occupies more land and has double the area to be roofed.

Above four storeys the unit cost will rise due to the need for a structural frame and more substantial foundations. On some sites pile foundations may be required. Whilst the proportional costs of the foundations and roof reduce as height increases they are more than offset by the construction costs such as hoists, scaffolding, tower cranes and the increase in services. However, costs such as those for tower cranes do not further increase with height once they are in place. Services installations increase unit cost due to the provision of lifts, larger service ducts, internal discharge pipes, rooftop gantry for external maintenance and fire protection. Furthermore, the provision of services reduces the usable floor area of the building which in turn increases unit cost. Fire protection is a major hazard with high rise buildings and therefore a sprinkler or wet riser system may have to be installed. A generator may also be required to provide emergency power should there be a power failure in the main supply.

It must be noted that many high rise buildings built in Britain have developed serious problems relating to frame and cladding stability and weather resistance. These problems have not been experienced in the USA with their steel framed skyscrapers.

Internal layout – Buildings vary in unit cost as the layout varies. Thus, both the usable floor area and number of internal walls and partitions must be considered carefully.

Specification – The quality of materials together with standard of workmanship required must be taken into account in order to evaluate any scheme. Another factor affecting cost is the use of standard components in preference to those which are purpose made. Where materials are scarce or have extensive delivery periods alternative materials may be considered.

Buildability – The availability of building components and ease of construction will influence building costs. Therefore, traditional construction may be more economical than non-traditional as may be the elimination or reduction of wet trades in the building process. Pre-fabricated components may also speed up site operations although they can be very expensive.

Pre-fabricated or system buildings have been used in Britain with varying degrees of success. High rise flats and timber framed houses were unsuccessful due to poor construction practices and SCOLA schools and the like suffered from economies of scale due to insufficient demand. However, the advantages of off-the-shelf steel framed industrial buildings are currently being successfully exploited by offering a limited number of standard designs. Here, standard units may be extended in length by adding additional bays, at a set cost per bay, or sideways with an identical or smaller standard unit.

In the early 1970s dimensional co-ordination was introduced into the building industry as part of metrication nationally. The idea was to design buildings to dimensions in multiples of 3 metres or divisible parts thereof. Thus, by manufacturing materials such as wall boards and building blocks to complementary sizes the need for cutting would be avoided thereby reducing time and cost. For both designers and builders the problems this created far outweighed any potential economies and as a result dimensional co-ordination was discontinued.

Other factors – Most schemes incorporate requirements peculiar to each respective client. For example, each hospital may in addition to standard services offer specialist heart or brain surgery. The nature of both the work and the equipment used to provide these special facilities often necessitates more innovated and complex building design. In a similar way external works and drainage requirements will vary with each project and therefore they too need to be individually evaluated.

Further, aspects such as location and contractual arrangements will affect cost especially the preliminaries as they are unique to each project in terms of both the specific requirements and the relative cost. Maintenance could well be an important issue to owner occupiers and therefore an appraisal of life cycle costs may have to be undertaken.

Factors influencing builders' costs   The cost to a builder of carrying out work varies due to a number of factors. These factors may be summarised as being location, quantity, quality, risk, time and method together with the level of resource costs. To some extent these factors are inter-linked, for example changes in quantity or quality will influence both the time taken to carry out the work and the subsequent costs incurred. Resource costs may be influenced in this manner but can also vary independently. Independent variations arise out of economic factors such as the supply of skilled operatives, the availability of materials and the workload levels of sub-contractors.

Location, quantity and quality of the work together with the time available for carrying out the work may influence the builder's method of construction. Alternatively, where the builder is required to offer a time for the building period, as part of the tender, then the method of construction may influence such an offer to the client. This explanation is over simplified to demonstrate how one factor may influence another.

In reality the situation is a little more complex as alternative methods of construction generally have different cost consequences for the builder. Costs are usually an important part of the tender therefore the builder must, where possible, balance the effect that each factor has on the other to arrive at the most competitive solution.

Other factors affecting builders costs include specification requirements, contractual arrangements and contract period.

Sources of cost data   Cost data may be obtained from a number of sources, each with a varying level of accuracy. The appropriateness of data sources depends on the method of estimating employed. For instance, most approximate estimating techniques rely heavily on historic rather than current prices. Thus, details of past tenders, especially the contents of priced bills of quantities relating to similar work, provide a suitable means by which cost yardsticks may be established.

More accurate estimating involves the individual pricing of work items, mainly by use of standard data applied to, or with, up to date costs. Standard data for labour and plant relate to production output, whereas those for materials relate to quantity requirements. Work items can basically be broken down into resource components of labour, materials and plant,[2] irrespective of whether the work is directly carried out by the builder or sub-contracted to others. Small firms dealing with a limited range of short duration work with a handful of operatives may find it easier to estimate costs. This is particularly so when considering operatives' outputs as the work-force to be used is generally the same for each job. Where the boss works alongside his employees it is possible to assess the actual ability of each operative.

Whilst the sources of cost data provide different levels of accuracy most practitioners involved with cost forecasting and prediction generally prefer to use their own data banks. This is because each practitioner has less confidence in the reliability of data produced by others.

The work item components and the available sources of cost data for each are as follows:

Labour cost	Material cost	Plant cost
Labour output	Material quantity	Plant output.

Labour cost: Federation notification of agreed minimum wage levels, also available from publications such as price books and journals

Builder's internal records of employment costs, comprising of wages, bonus, cost control and similar feedback

Quotations from labour-only sub-contractors

An individual's knowledge and experience.

All but an individual's expertise (variable attribute) should provide up to date factual information although the federation wage levels only form part of the builder's cost of employing an operative. The problems that may be encountered with some internal data arise from the level of expertise of both those providing the mass of data and those analysing and reducing such data in order to produce manageable statistics.

Labour output: Internal records of standards compiled over many years

An individual's expertise

Information derived from internal feedback

Work study or less formal checks on the time taken by operatives to carry out specific operations

Published data.

All but published data and expertise should provide realistic information for each individual company as the data represents the outputs of the operatives employed, or the outputs that their operatives are expected to achieve. The accuracy of the outputs used and the likelihood that other builders use differing outputs are both separate issues relating to the difference in costs incurred by each individual builder when comparing one with another.

Work study is of particular importance. Its purpose is to reduce costs by increasing efficiency.[3] One activity within work study involves establishing the time that operatives take to carry out specific operations of work. The data is derived by observing and recording the operations whilst they are being carried out on site. Work study may also be used to provide both an appraisal of productivity levels and a critical examination of each operation to determine the most effective method of working.

Note that internal records are reviewed and up dated periodically as more data is collected.

Material cost: Quotations from suppliers

Invoices for materials purchased

Costs obtained from previous jobs

Published data

An individual's expertise.

New quotations from suppliers that relate to specific jobs are the most reliable source, especially where immediate orders are to be placed. However, where they are obtained for tendering purposes there is a good chance that the cost of materials will increase by the time they are required on site. Attention must be given to this where a firm price tender is required or when providing cost advice. Current invoices are another good source although not always as reliable due to the fact that with many materials the amount charged by suppliers varies with size of order and haulage distances.

Old quotations, invoices and cost data are inherently less reliable as up dating can only be approximate. Published data is the least reliable because it offers only an indication of future price levels based on a national average of suppliers prices. Data is usually published on say a quarterly or annual basis, calculated by averaging predicted future changes in average prices nationally. Published data is therefore not very reliable as it does not represent the actual costs of materials to be incurred by any individual builder due to the different prices on offer within each region.

Particulars of past projects are available to subscribers from the RICS Building Cost Information Service (BCIS). These particulars include contractual arrangements, tendering procedures and complete cost analysis. Other information available includes average building prices, briefing, building index series and news. There is also an on-line service available which enables users to request and receive such information, this being down-loaded onto a computer via a telephone and modem. There are two main disadvantages with BICS cost analyses, these being:

1   appropriate information may not be available as the range of projects on offer is dependent on analyses obtained from subscribers

2   consultants are less confident in using information compiled by other parties. This is due to the absence of first hand knowledge of the project and the manner in which the analysis is produced.

Where prices are not available or when dealing with sundry items or if using published data as a cost guide then the cost may sometimes be guessed. This is usually an educated guess based on a sound knowledge of current price levels within the industry. Expertise are therefore potentially more reliable than published data in some circumstances.

Material quantity: Internal records of standard quantity allowances

An individual's expertise

Information derived from internal feedback

Published data.

All should provide a reasonable indication of quantity

requirements necessary to carry out the work although, as with labour output, the builder's own records are more factual. This is especially so for the assessment of some aspects of material quantities such as that for wastage allowances.

Plant cost: Quotations from plant-hire firms

Invoices for hired plant

Costs obtained from previous jobs

Published data

An individual's experience.

The appropriateness of these sources is the same as that described for material cost.

Plant output: The sources and their appropriateness are similar to that described for labour output.

Approaches to estimating

Approximate estimating   Quantity surveyors mainly employ approximate estimating techniques to provide the client with an indication of the likely building cost. Similarly builders use these techniques in order to produce early cost estimates and provide cost advice. However, speculative house builders, management contractors and those involved with design and build are more likely to be involved with such techniques. It must be noted that as designers' estimating techniques rely heavily on historic prices it is essential that the data is up dated by applying adjustments for differences in quantity, quality, location and price.

There are a number of techniques available and as they require differing levels of design information their relative accuracy varies.[4] The choice of technique(s) to be used in each situation is therefore dependent on the level of accuracy required and the extent to which the design has been developed, ie the quality of information available. In order that early cost advice can be given it is necessary to know either how much the client intends to spend or an indication of building size and type required.

An outline of designers' approximate estimating techniques[5] and their relative accuracy are as follows:

Cost per unit

This utilises the relationship between a building and its functional units for projects where the number of units can initially be identified. Certain categories of buildings such as car parks (including multi-storey), schools, and hospitals are suited to this method, functional units being the number of parking spaces, beds, pupils and beds respectively.

Here, unit costs derived from previous jobs are adjusted and used to forecast the cost of current projects. The principle is very simple but the practicalities are complex as most buildings are unique in design. Thus, account must be taken of factors such as building shape and storey height. This is a speedy although very crude method of establishing a budget figure.

> EXAMPLE: Data from previous car park—
> Total cost $\quad\quad$ £500,000
> Number of spaces $\quad$ 500
> Cost per unit $= \dfrac{£500,000}{500} = £1,000$

> Proposed car park offers 850 spaces—
> Cost per space adjusted for quantity, quality, location and price $= £1,100$
> COST FORECAST $= 850 \times £1100 = \underline{£935,000}$

Note that this calculation would not be valid where the proposed car park is totally or partly underground.

Cost per square metre

This utilises the relationship between a building and its floor area, measured between the inside of external walls with no deductions for internal walls and the like. The technique operates on a similar principle to that of the unit method but using the internal floor area in lieu of the functional unit. Abnormal features such as lifts and non standard foundations are adjusted on a lump sum basis and added to the total building cost.

It is relatively easy to use at the early stages as it requires little information other than outline drawings. Due to its ease of use practitioners have developed large data sources and as a result has become a very popular technique. The technique is potentially more accurate than other early methods, especially if based on projects of similar type and size.

Cost per cubic metre

This is similar to the square metre method but based on building volume. Different rules apply for calculating the volume. Being more difficult to apply, the method has been abandoned in favour of the method previously mentioned.

Storey enclosure

This is another method which has been abandoned. Again it is very similar to the square metre method but as each floor (or basement) level is measured they are adjusted by a weighting factor. The intention is to derive a global cost per square metre which takes account of cost differentials between low and high rise buildings.

Approximate quantities

This involves the measuring and pricing of work in the traditional manner. However, the scope of measurement is limited to cost significant items. Those items with common dimensions are dealt with collectively. Thus, the measurement for superstructure external walls, expressed in square metres, may incorporate internal and external skins, forming cavity and ties, internal plaster and decorative finish. An appropriate composite rate per square metre is then applied. In the event that decorative wall finishes differ throughout the building (paint, paper, tiles) it may be simpler to measure decorations separately. Sundry items are accounted for by adjusting the composite rate.

It is recommended that the measurement is carried out by the person who will be pricing the work so that possible omissions and misunderstandings, as to what is included in an item, are minimised. Pricing is generally based on data from previous projects.

Builders may produce approximate quantities where bills of quantities are not provided. Here, builders are more likely to calculate new rates from first principles rather than using rates from previous projects. Where time does not allow new calculations then the alternative must be considered.

This technique is more time consuming than those previously outlined although a much greater level of accuracy should be attained. Because it also requires more design details than the others it cannot be used during project brief. Cost targets must therefore be determined by early estimating techniques, unless set initially by the client.

Elemental estimating

This is an alternative to the approximate quantities technique. It involves separating the project into standard building elements such as frame, upper floors, roof, external walls and subsequently pricing each element using comparable elemental costs obtained from similar projects derived by elemental cost analysis.*

* This involves analysing projects in order to provide data for future cost planning activity. Projects are separated into standard elements and the cost of each element is established, from builders' cost breakdowns, and converted into a cost per square metre of gross floor area.

The technique makes use of the advantages associated with the square metre method in that the pricing data for each element is presented as a cost per square metre of gross floor area in addition to the elemental cost. Each element is considered in turn and adjustments made for quantity, quality, location and price up-date. Price adjustments may be taken into account at each stage of the process or alternatively as a single adjustment at the end. Adjustment for quantity is usually a complex and time consuming operation which may be difficult for the estimator to control. The total of each elemental cost per square metre is multiplied by the gross floor area of the proposed project to establish total building cost.

Cost planning and control   In the past, cost forecasting techniques were not very sophisticated due mainly to the fact that buildings remained predominantly traditional both in design and specification. This state of equilibrium no longer existed after the Second World War because of the need to meet the huge demand for building work. New designs, materials and construction methods were introduced in order to satisfy demand economically.

Clients subsequently required an accurate forecast of building costs in advance of making any financial commitments. Cost forecasting therefore had not only to meet this objective but also to incorporate ways in which costs could be monitored and controlled throughout the design period in order that client requirements were satisfied. As a result both cost planning and cost control systems were introduced.

Cost control

This is implemented throughout the building process from inception to completion in the form of pre and post contract activities. During the design and tendering periods the activity focuses on cost forecasting and control of design development to produce both a satisfactory scheme and suitable contractor procurement. During the building period the cost of each element is monitored and adjusted as design changes are made in order to provide the client with up to date cost information and advice. The prices contained in the builder's tender form the basis for post contract cost control.

Cost planning

This is a technique which provides the vehicle for cost control during the design period. Various estimating techniques may be used in cost planning although elemental techniques are generally preferred once the target (goal) has been set. Setting the most advantageous cost target to each element facilitates development of a balanced design and thereby attaining the best value solution.

Elemental estimating, as described earlier, was initially developed for this purpose. Contrary to opinion the technique is currently only used by a few quantity surveying offices. However, elemental estimating still exists but in an amended form. This amended form remains in principle the same as that described earlier but incorporates the approximate quantities technique. The result is that each element is more accurately represented and the need for complex quantity adjustments is eliminated. Elemental costs are established by using cost data contained in bills of quantities and other similar sources or publications. Analytical estimating techniques may be applied to certain items especially where published data is either inappropriate or unavailable.

Cost targets (budgets) may be established either by estimating the cost of alternative design solutions or by comparing the costs of similar buildings or by forecasting rental or capital value. Alternatively, budgets may be imposed either by the client's available funds or by specific design requirements or even by limits set by central and local government. Thus, design development may be centred on either cost or design, depending on whether the client's brief involves designing to a cost or costing to a design[6] respectively. Whilst the two have different goals elemental cost planning is common to both.

The pre-contract estimating process is as follows:

Design stage	*Action to be taken*
Feasibility	Single rate estimate – cost per unit or square metre
Outline proposals	Elemental cost plan. This may involve establishing costs for alternative design solutions
Scheme design	Cost checks – as the design is developed the cost of each element is compared to ensure that the element budget is not exceeded
Detailed design	Final check. Full bills of quantities may be priced later (pre-tender estimate)
Acceptance of tender	Cost analysis (elemental).

Estimating from first principles Builders mainly use cost and production based estimating techniques to determine the likely cost of carrying out the building work with the greatest possible accuracy. The process is carried out during the tendering period using the most realistic sources of data available. A builder is usually better equipped than a consultant to produce reasonably accurate results using cost related estimating techniques due to the relentless time and effort devoted to the activity. Further, a builder is in a position to know more about his costs and gross profit requirements than those outside the firm.

Small builders and sub-contractors may price work on the spot. Here, a painter and decorator may enter a room and, as a result of a visual assessment of the work, give a quotation. Where unusual finishings are required such an approach will be unlikely. On the spot pricing is only possible when the range of work is very small, relatively constant and carried out frequently. Alternatively, some small builders and many sub-contractors produce cost estimates by pricing large sections of the work in their entirety, the sum of the sections being the total project cost. Further, the total labour cost may be established in one global assessment rather than in sections. the reason for this is either that they are never required to price bills of quantities or that they find difficulty in calculating prices on a unit rate basis. A unit rate is the cost of carrying out a work item per measured unit such as per cubic metre of concrete or per square metre of brickwork.

Other organisations are more likely to adopt a different approach as a high proportion of projects for which they tender are let on bills of quantities. The format of bills is such that estimators need to have the ability to identify the operations to which each work item belongs from a large number of individually described work items, plus the ability to cope with single quantities rather than totals. As builders' estimators are accustomed to this it is not surprising that they produce their own bills when not provided as a tender document.

An outline of estimating techniques used by builder's estimators[7] are as follows:

Analytical estimating

This is the most popular technique used by estimators for predicting costs of the builder's own work within a project. As the normal practice is to price bills of quantities, firm or approximate, a unit rate has to be established for each item of measured work. Therefore the estimator normally reduces all relevant data to a unit equivalent and calculations are made on that basis. Standard data such as labour or plant outputs and material requirements are recorded in unit equivalents for ease of use. Note that labour, materials and plant are referred to as *resources*.

Unit rates may be calculated net or inclusive of overheads and profit, at the builder's discretion. The net cost approach has been adopted in this text.

EXAMPLE
Excavate foundation trench .... 60 m³
Standard data – JCB3c output 0.16 hours/m³
Required data – cost of JCB + driver and fuel
$$=£12/hour^*$$
cost of lorry + driver and fuel
$$= £11.50/hour^*$$
cost of banksman = £4.61/hour*

Rate build-up   m³
JCB   .16 × £12   = 1.92
lorry .16 × £11.50 = 1.84
b/man.16 × £4.61   = 0.74
Unit rate 4.50

* These are resource all-in rates, consisting of the basic cost of employment or hire plus other costs incurred by the builder. Calculations to establish all-in rates have been excluded from this example.

The unit rate is then inserted in the bill of quantities:

Excavate foundation trench | 60 m³ | 4.50 | 270.00.

An alternative approach using the same technique would be to price the total quantity and then divide by 60 m³:

Total time 60 × .16 = 9.6 hours
Total cost per hour = 12 + 11.5 + 4.61 = £28.11
Total cost of item = 9.6 × £28.11 = £269.86
Unit rate = £269.86 = £4.50/m³
            60

The rate build-up formats shown above are adequate for later reference and can be entered on the blank page opposite the bill page containing the item.

Where the calculation is entered on a separate sheet an alternative method of recording the information in the bill is the six column method. Here, resource unit costs, grouped together, are entered in a standard sequence under the item that is being priced:

Resources and tabulation sequence

labour	plant	materials	subcontract	overheads/profit

EXAMPLE (based on previously calculated excavation item)

0.74	3.76				

This allows arithmetic checks of all page totals and the final total. The total value of each resource contained in the final total can also be calculated. Unfortunately a more detailed analysis of labour or plant is not possible. As a result, data cannot be produced to aid the planning process other than a general resource programme.

Such limitations are overcome with the use of estimating slips as shown in figure 3.1. The size of the slips can be altered to suit individual needs and to accommodate the level of complexity associated with the items to be priced. The left half of the slip plus the item description, reference and quantity can be filled in by the estimator leaving the right hand side for an assistant to complete. The assistant may reference all the slips in advance although this is not recommended. Also the assistant may carry out the arithmetic calculations to the left of the slip and possibly enter the rate into the bill. Again this is not recommended.

Trench excavation n.e. 1m deep							Item ref. 3/23/f					
Resource	Plant	lab	mat	rate	£	p	Quants	P	L	M	£	p
JCB3c	.16			£12hr	1	92	60	9.6			115	20
lorry	.16			£11.5	1	84		9.6			110	40
Tradesman												
Labourer		.16		£4.61		74			9.6		44	26
Rate per....m3 ......£					4	50	Totals...cost £				269	86

Figure 3.1   Estimating slip

The slip method enables total hours and total material quantities to be established for each component of an item and also total values for the project. For example, the total time allowed for lorries, excavators, dumpers, tradesmen and labourers can be individually calculated and the cost of each identified. A similar analysis can also be carried out for each material. It is usually impossible to provide this level of detail either at pre-tender or post contract unless a computer aided system is used.

Operational estimating

This is not as popular with builder's estimators although very popular with those estimators employed by civil engineers due to the nature of their work. The technique requires a different approach to that of analytical estimating and is suitable for pricing work which involves a combination of resources and a number of activities. Typical builders' operations where this technique may be used are:

> *earthworks* – a variety of excavators, dumpers, lorries and labour may be required

> *in situ reinforced concrete suspended floor slabs* – each floor involves formwork, reinforcement, concrete, stripping form-work and back propping (unless quick release systems are used).

Here, the production resources (labour and plant) are deter-mined by establishing the amount of work that has to be carried out and relating the required work output to the duration allocated to the operation. The cost of these resources is then calculated on a time basis in accordance with the overall duration shown on the programme. Materials are calculated separately. Separate calcula-tions to determine idle time are avoided as this is automatically taken into account in the overall duration. Checks must, however, be carried out to ensure that the production resources can match the required outputs.

With, for example, excavation work where the volume of earth to be moved is 16,000 cubic metres and the construction programme indicates an eight week duration, then the target is 2,000 m^3 per week. To achieve this target it may be necessary to have a combination of four earth moving machines, three dumpers, five lorries and two banksmen. The total cost of the operation is calculated by multiplying the total weekly cost of resources by eight weeks. A unit rate per cubic metre may then be obtained by dividing the cost of the operation by 16,000. Where specific resources are not fully occupied but are required to be at hand throughout the operation then the full cost of such resources are automatically included in the one calculation.

Spot items

A spot item relates more to the way in which work is measured and described rather than an estimating technique, although they invariably require an approach different from that used for other items of measured work. These items are those which the quantity surveyor is not able to measure either accurately or in detail, such as the forming of an opening in an existing wall including inserting a lintel and making good to both brick and plaster work. Here, the builder must make an assessment of the work involved in order to calculate a suitable lump sum price. A site visit will enable the condition of the wall, type of bricks and blocks, associated finishings, working restrictions and the like to be established. However, the amount of plaster to be made good may vary depending on how much care is taken in carrying out the work together with the condition of the plaster.

When pricing, the builder must take into account all the operations necessary to complete the work including staging, propping to the existing structure and any need for dust screens to protect the existing internal area. The resources may be priced on the basis of separate activities or establish approximate quantities for each item within the operation.

Domestic sub-contractors' quotations

A builder may sub-let his work to other organisations subject to the architects approval. Quotations from potential sub-contractors are therefore obtained during the tender period and the most competitive and acceptable bids are selected. The rates contained in these quotations, with any appropriate adjustments or additions, are then entered into the bill of quantities. For work which is not traditionally sub-let the estimator will prepare his own estimate of the work and subsequently compare it with quotations received.

Accuracy of builders' estimates   The accuracy of estimates produced is generally proportional to the amount of time devoted to the activity, the applied level of detail and the estimating technique used together with the peculiarities associated with specific projects such as complexity and accuracy of tender documentation. Assuming that good practice is followed there is no reason why high levels of accuracy cannot be achieved. However, the levels of accuracy associated with repetitive factory production are not possible in building as each project is unique in terms of either production activity and/or contractual arrangements. Further, estimating not only involves pricing the physical parts of a building but also all the indirect work and services associated with contracting.

Builders' estimates are therefore inherently inaccurate, the level of which can only be crudely judged by comparative methods. An early assessment may be made using the tender prices submitted by other builders as a yardstick. Another assessment can be carried out post contract by using the actual costs incurred on site as a basis for comparison. Both methods have their limitations irrespective of their popularity. There are numerous reasons why actual cost differs from estimated cost, many of which are completely unrelated to the accuracy of the original estimate, so much so that one estimate may be nearer to actual cost than another more accurate estimate.

Sources of estimating inaccuracy   Builders' estimating techniques are unlikely to produce completely accurate estimates. It is for this reason that some may argue that such techniques are approximate. The main factors which give rise to inaccuracies are outlined as follows:

Human errors – *arithmetic, transcription, transposition* [8], *preparing own quantities where bills not provide*

Expertise   – *judgement and experience required for pricing much of the work – how much to allow for protection items and winter working, sundry items may be guessed**

Prediction   – *varying ability of operatives, resource outputs fluctuate, labour problems, failure by suppliers and sub-contractors to fulfil their obligations, work carried out under changed circumstances, assessing site waste, firm price adjustment, adverse weather, possible contract overrun, making good defects after liability period*

Data   – *use of averaged output data, inadequate site feedback data, insufficient or inadequate tender information*

Time   – *inadequate tender period and consequently insufficient time available for estimating, lost time due to bill preparation for plan and specification work, inaccurate measurement with plan and specification.*

---

* This may relate to the 80/20 concept where approximately 80% of cost is contained in 20% of the work items. Thus 20% of builders work may be given scant consideration. Some builders are prepared to accept this yet haggle for hours over waste allowance levels – 5% or 7.5%?

References

1 DUNCAN WALLACE, I N, *Hudson's building and civil engineering contracts*, Sweet and Maxwell 1970, tenth edition, pp 5, 7–8.
2 COOKE, B, *Contract planning and contractual procedures*, Macmillan 1981, pp 39–41.
3 OXLEY, R, and POSKILL, J, *Management techniques applied to the construction industry*, fourth edition, Collins 1986, pp 171.
4 ASHWORTH, A, and SKITMORE, R M, 'Accuracy in estimating', CIOB, Occasional paper, no. 27, pp 6–11.
5 SEELEY, I H, *Building economics*, Macmillan 1972, pp 103–124.
6 BATHURST, P E, and BUTLER, D A, *Building cost control techniques and economics*, second edition, Heinemann 1980, pp 99–106.
7 CIOB, *Code of estimating practice*, fifth edition, CIOB 1983, pp 74, 81–3.
8 BRIGGS, T, 'Modulus 11 check digit systems', *The Computer Bulletin*, vol. 14, no. 8, August 1970, pp 266–9.

Questions

1 During times of strong competition, contractors have maintained constant tender levels although there have been significant increases in the costs of resources.

Examine this phenomenon with regard to the contractor's reaction to market forces and the subsequent changes in production procedures.

2 Critically compare approximate quantities with elemental cost analysis as methods of cost appraisal used during the later design stages.

3 Discuss the factors to be considered in the economic design of a building.

4 Cost forecasting techniques are unreliable to the extent that a client will not know the true cost of a building until the competitive tenders are received.

Discuss this statement.

4 Tendering

Tender documents

Purpose and types of tender documents Tender documents are intended to provide each builder with common data in sufficient detail to suit the circumstances of each project. The intention with such documents is to obtain a number of competitive tenders that can be compared objectively in order to select a suitable bidder. Certain information for specific projects may be approximate or notional where design cannot be completed or where a number of similar jobs are to be let, using one set of documentation, respectively. In these circumstances it is important to produce definitive documents as they provide a common basis for both tendering and price adjustment at a later date.

Where tenders are accepted without amendment the tender documents may become part of the contract documents. In some cases the bid may be amended by the client prior to entering into a contract, and if documents are adjusted or amended such changes would be incorporated into the contract documents. This may arise when, for instance, bids exceed the client's budget and bills of reductions are introduced in order to bring the contract sum within budget. In liaison with the builder reductions may be achieved through changes in quantity and or quality of work, eg reduce the overall size of the building or omit specific parts thereof, omit carpets and other floor finishes or change the specification to something cheaper.

Due to the various arrangements and procurement routes in existence there are numerous tender documents and combinations thereof just as there are many forms of contract and alternative contract document permutations. Common tender documents in use are drawings and form of tender, with a reply envelope, accompanied by a specification. A schedule of rates may also be used in conjunction with these documents or alternatively a bill of quantities (firm or approximate).

Where bills are used there is no need for a separate specification. If the relevant schedule of rates is the PSA's own pre-priced document then this will have to be purchased by the builder unless already done so. Tender documents are issued to the builder with an accompanying letter which contains tendering instructions, a list of enclosures (the documents issued) and the date for tender submission. The list enables the builder to check that he is in possession of all the documents.

The tender must be received by the client no later than the date specified and, if applicable, by an appointed time. That which is finally presented to the client must be returned in the official addressed envelope provided along with the completed form of tender. Traditional arrangements often only require the return of the tender form.

In addition to the client's data the builder may be required to generate other information which will be presented to the client along with the form of tender as part of the bid. This is certainly true with design and build, joint venture, the BPF system and many management contracts. Further data may include a method statement, construction programme and contract sum analysis. Although the way this works in practice varies with each job an outline of specific approaches, obtained from leading national contractors in their respective field, are as follows:

Design and build – From the client's brief (employer's requirements) the builder produces drawings which define the work, specification, construction programme and method statement, then calculates the price to be charged. The price is presented in the form of an elemental cost breakdown, collectively named the contract sum analysis. With the exception of the method statement which is not always included, all the data (contractor's proposals) is submitted to the client as the builder's bid.

Usually an approximate elemental bill of quantities is prepared by the builder to assist in establishing the tender sum and subsequent preparation of the contract sum analysis. A copy of the priced bill may be given to the client on the condition that the quantities and rates are not challenged. This proviso is for two reasons, (i) the contract is lump sum, (ii) the accuracy of the quantities is not open to debate even though the builder tends to over measure* rather than under measure the work due to limited time available.

Management contracting – Tender documents issued to the contractor include a brief description of the project, drawings, brief specification, cost plan and an indication of project duration. The cost plan is in work section format, each representing the likely

---

* This should not be frowned upon, after all if the builder is awarded the contract it will have been obtained in competition with others. Another point is that any loss of monies arising through errors in measurement have to be absorbed by the builder. For example, one large builder was awarded a number of identical design and build contracts. Here, the builder employed another organisation to prepare a bill of quantities and subsequently used it to prepared the bids. It was later discovered that certain sections of work had not been measured, the value of which (builder's loss) amounted to more than 10% of the contract sum for each project awarded.

work packages required to complete the building work. On this occasion the contractors bid broadly covers the following:

expertise – a statement of experience and expertise within the organisation followed by details of the management approach to be employed on this particular project.

duration – programmes for both the building work and staff deployment. The complement of staff allocated to the project includes a quality assurance officer. The building programme enables the contractor to determine whether a building period can be offered which is shorter than that indicated by the client.

production – Details of the method of construction.

fee – The financial reimbursement required for managerial services and a separate sum to cover for providing both common site facilities and a supportive general workforce (jobbing gang). This is followed by a report on the validity of the client's cost plan. One technique which may be used to achieve this involves comparing the cost of each package with costs for similar packages on other projects. The report also identifies packages that either have not been accounted for or provide scope for splitting into further packages.

The manager is paid by the client on a monthly basis, or as otherwise agreed, in accordance with the amount of work carried out. As sub-contracts are formed with the manager all payments to sub-contractors are via the manager. Provision is made for the manager to claim fluctuations in costs relating to site staff. On this project the chain of command is client, architect, manager, sub-contractor.

Bills of quantities   Bills of quantities (BQs) are a form of schedule with quantities, incorporating *preliminaries* and *preambles* sections. They provide builders with a wealth of information about the contract in addition to the detailed breakdown of the proposed work. Where bills are not required as tender or contract documents it is quite likely that some of the data contained therein must still be conveyed to those tendering by means of alternative documentation. Information often required includes specification details and contract particulars.

For the builder, a bill provides a comprehensive list of work items and other information that can be replicated for issue to organisations in order to obtain quotations and is also readily used for pricing the work in detail. Once the contract commences the document can be used on site to supplement information shown on drawings and is in sufficient detail to be used for cost control, determining periodic payments and the settlement of variations and extras. For the client it provides an itemised breakdown of cost which can be referred to at any time to ensure that progress payments and variation accounts are accurately valued.

When a bill of quantities is not provided by the client the builder is likely to prepare his own, the measured work section together with the Prime Cost (PC) and provisional sums, where applicable, forming the main part of such a document.

A review of the contents of a bill of quantities as follows is useful in that it generally covers the scope of tender documentation alternatives that may have to be provided when dispensing with bills of quantities:

Preliminaries
The preliminaries section contains the following:

the project generally – project particulars relating to the client, architect, quantity surveyor, drawings, an outline of the site and description of the work

the contract – a list of the applicable conditions of contract and appendix data

employer's requirements – details relating to tendering additional to those on the invitation to tender, sub-letting, provision and content of documents, management of the works, quality control, security, safety, working restrictions, facilities to be provided for the client's benefit and building maintenance

contractor's general cost items – items that the builder must provide for the proper running of the site such as management, site accommodation, services, facilities, mechanical plant and temporary works

work by others or subject to instruction – work or materials arranged directly by the client or at his instruction: work by statutory bodies, nominated sub-contractors and suppliers, provisional work including dayworks.

Each item of information may or may not have cost implications and therefore provision is made for the builder to enter a price against each if so required. The builder must consider each item carefully as the implications of many can vary for different projects.

Where the proposed form of contract contains specific clauses which offer a choice from a number of alternatives, such as insurance for the works, the alternative that is to be implemented by the client must be stated. Other conditions peculiar to the particular project must also be described. These include the limit of insurance cover, retention percentage, dates for possession and completion of the works, period of interim payments, fluctuations, requirement of a bond* and other such matters which will affect the builder's costs and level of risk.

Where specifications are used without bills of quantities then details concerning preliminary items may be either incorporated into the specification document or contained in a separate document. Whichever option is used whilst the preliminaries will not be covered in as much detail as that contained in a bill all matters affecting both the tender price and the proposed contract will be identified.

Preambles

The preambles section contains details of the specification in terms of the work, the workmanship and materials together with any further information that may qualify the scope and interpretation of work item descriptions including deviations from standard conventions. The provision of a bill of quantities therefore eliminates the need for a separate specification document. With local authority contracts specific reference is usually made to the council's standard specification which covers in detail the full range of building work. It is important to ensure that work is priced in accordance with the requirements of these documents especially where the local authority specification dictates higher performance standards.

Often there is ambiguity in the requirements of measured work items as in the case of hardcore fill. Broken brick or limestone may generally be used as hardcore although the former is often cheaper, depending on availability. However, before pricing such an item reference must be made to the preambles section, relating to filling materials, as limestone may be specified. In this case pricing for broken brick would lead to considerable loss of money on the activity as the architect would insist on either the use of limestone or a cost saving for the client.

Measured work

This section contains details of the direct work required to be carried out and mainly represents the actual components of the final building. There are of course some exceptions to this which relate to preparation work such as the excavation of trenches to accommodate the foundations and also to temporary work such as supporting

---

* This generally indemnifies the client in respect of a percentage of the contract sum, normally 10%, should the builder fail to complete the works (different bonds are available). As bonds are normally arranged with the bank, the builder's credit facility is reduced by the recovery value of the bond. Thus, there is a limit to the number of jobs requiring bonds that many builders can undertake.

trenches with props and erecting shuttering to retain concrete until it has hardened.

Each item of work is listed separately and consists of a description, unit of measurement and quantity with spaces to the side to enable the builder to insert his unit rate and total price thereof. The items are often grouped into work sections responding to the order set out in the relevant SMM.

An alternative to this is elemental format where the super-structure of a building is split into major elements such as upper floors, roof, stairs, external walls, windows and external doors. However, within each element the order of items follows work section sequence. This format is useful to builders in the planning of the work and to those involved with cost analysis data and is becoming more popular with builders involved with design and build where a contract sum analysis has to be prepared.

Prime Cost and Provisional Sums, Dayworks and Contingency
These are contained in many BQs and are subject to instruction by the architect. They are dealt with as follows:

Prime cost sums – Prime cost relates to work which is to be carried out by sub-contractors or suppliers selected by the architect. This selection procedure is referred to as nomination, hence the term nominated sub-contractor. Remember that under the JCT Intermediate Form of Contract and with Contractor Design there is provision for naming but not for nominating. Any specialist work may be the subject of nomination, for example: lift installation, structural steelwork, suspended ceilings, electrical installations, heating and ventilation installations. Materials such as ironmongery or bricks may also be subject to nomination although bricks are dealt with differently. Here the value of the PC sum is given in the description of the item in the measured work section, not as a separate item under PCs. The value of each PC, estimated by the architect, is incorporated into the bill, during bill production, in the cash column. This sum represents the notional cost to the builder for the item described and is inclusive of a cash discount. With the exception of those that abuse the credit system builders pay on a monthly account basis in order to qualify for any specified discount, this basically acts as an incentive for early payment. The discount is 2.5% for sub-contractors and 5% for suppliers. The description of each nominated sub-contract is followed by separate items for profit, general attendance and possibly special attendance. The builder enters in the cash column the monies required for each of the separate items, therefore the section is a competitive element of the tender.

General attendance to be provided by the builder is in accordance with SMM7 rule A 11 C3 and any additional requirements are deemed to be special attendance. Note that each special attendance item must be shown separately to allow the builder to price individually. These items should be described in sufficient detail as to enable the builder to price adequately.

It is often difficult to price some special attendance items, for example in relation to heating and ventilation work the requirement may be to unload, store, distribute, unpack, hoist and place in position all items of fittings and equipment. If taken literally this leaves very little for the sub-contractor to do. However, the real problem for the builder arises from not having details of the quantity, size, and weight of the sub-contract materials. Also, the relationship between the builder and the sub-contractor may become strained if the sub-contractor needs to hoist temporarily and mark out prior to hoisting for final fixing. As the builder will have only allowed for hoisting once, in accordance with the special attendance item, the sub-contractor should be charged further hoisting.

Prior to entering into a contract with a nominated sub-contractor the builder should ensure that the full cash discount is offered and special attendance requirements do not exceed those described in the tender documents. In this instance the builder must refuse to sign the contract until such times as the architect, in writing, agrees either to omit the additional items or pay the builder for the extra costs involved. The builder should also check that the specialist's daywork rates do not exceed his own. If the rates are higher than his own then he should obtain an agreement in writing from the architect confirming that the builder shall be paid daywork at the specialist's rates, not the builder's, with a one thirty-ninth addition to cover the 2.5% m.a. entitlement.

Often the daywork rates are not submitted with the sub-contract details therefore the architect must be notified immediately, in writing, that contracts will not be entered into until such information is received. Protecting the builder's entitlement is unfortunately such that they could well be lost if these points are not ratified before signing nominated sub-contract forms.

PCs for material supply are more straightforward as each is followed only by an item for profit. The 'fix only' items associated with the materials will be contained in the measured work section of the bill. Although the offloading and storing of these materials is not dealt with as a specific item it will have to be carried out by the builder and such costs must therefore be accounted for.

Provisional sums – Where work cannot be fully measured and priced or defined in sufficient detail it may become the subject of a provisional sum. Where for instance, the extent of repairs to existing stone jambs and cills is difficult to ascertain it could become a provisional sum. The architect would insert into the cash column the amount of money allocated for carrying out the work. The sum includes contractors' mark-up and therefore the builder is not required to make any price adjustments or additions to these items. Work in relation to provisional sums may not necessarily be carried out by the builder as the expenditure of such monies is at the discretion of the architect.

Where items marked Approximate Quantity (provisional) are contained in the measured work section of the bill such reference relates to the fact that the descriptions or quantities may later be altered. The builder's unit rates are not provisional. One common example of this is the provision in the excavation section for breaking up rock, the quantity being unknown until the excavation work is complete. The builder is paid for the actual volume of rock excavated at the bill rate.

Dayworks – Dayworks relate to the method by which the builder is paid for carrying out all additional work ordered by the architect during the contract that cannot be properly measured and valued using original or adjusted bill rates. Sub-contractors may occasionally be presented with daywork charges from the builder for carrying out work on behalf of the sub-contractors. This often happens when sub-contractors arrange for their materials to be delivered to site but fail to send workmen to offload the goods or refuse to clear away debris left by their operatives.

The bill contains notional monies for labour, materials and plant. Under each of the three components there is provision for the builder to insert a percentage addition. The percentage addition must cover all monies required by the builder over and above the prime (net) cost to the builder, the prime cost for each component being in accordance with that described in the Definition of Prime Cost of Dayworks carried out under a Building Contract. The percentage addition is therefore another competitive element of the tender. The components are dealt with as follows:

Labour – prime cost is made up of the sum of the operative's guaranteed wage plus other agreed payments plus extra payment for skill, etc, plus public holiday payments plus employer's national insurance, annual holiday and death benefit scheme contributions plus statutory contributions made by the employer.

The incidental costs, overheads and profit are covered by the percentage addition which is normally in the region of 130 to 150%. If the percentage differs for the various categories of operatives such as joiner, labourer, lorry driver, then the builder must decide which is the most appropriate percentage to apply. The final decision is little more than a guess. Note that supervisory staff employed on the tools are paid at the prime cost of labour applicable to the trade they are engaged in.

Materials – prime cost is the cost of materials delivered to site less all discounts other than a cash discount of 5%. Alternatively the prime cost of materials supplied from the builder's stock is the current market price plus necessary handling charges.

The builder decides the percentage addition required to cover incidental costs, overheads and profit. This addition is normally in the region of 10 to 15%.

Plant – prime cost is as provided by the contract. A common arrangement is that net plant costs are valued in accordance with the current Schedule of Basic Plant Charges issued by the Royal Institution of Chartered Surveyors. The schedule is revised periodically, five to ten years, and covers mechanical and non-mechanical plant rates including electrically operated plant and equipment but exclusive of drivers and attendants. Such operatives are claimed under the section governing labour. The schedule is intended to serve as a base index and therefore the prices contained therein do not reflect current market charges or hire rates.

The builder must decide on the percentage addition that is to be inserted into the bill. It is not difficult to establish the percentage difference between current hire rates and those in the schedule. However, this difference is likely to vary with each item of plant. Which percentage should the builder choose? The plant that is most likely to be used for daywork is the obvious choice but is impossible to identify with any certainty until daywork commences.

The rates in the schedule apply to plant already on site and not plant brought to site and specifically hired for daywork. Rates for plant brought specifically to site should cover the cost of hire including any transport to site and back plus an appropriate percentage to cover for incidental costs, overheads and profit. Rates not covered in the schedule should be agreed at amounts consistent with those in the schedule plus the builder's percentage addition as stated in the bill.

Contingency – A contingency is an amount of money inserted into the bill by the architect to be used by him as considered necessary. Such sums are usually expended on work which is either unforeseen or unaccounted for in the tender documentation. The sum is therefore generally used as a buffer to offset some affects of cost escalation. The builder is not required to make any price adjustments or additions to the contingency sum.

Co-ordinated project information (CPI) and the common arrangement   The building industry intends to introduce a system of co-ordinating the production of project information supplied to builders. The aim of this initiative is to improve the standard, accuracy, clarity and relevance of information by both the standardisation of documented data and the cross-referencing of data between documents. However, the success of CPI could well dependent on the willingness of design consultants to adopt the system. Note that the Co-ordinating Committee for Project Information has published the CPI for building works, a guide with examples details how CPI will be applied by each discipline.

The co-ordination of information is becoming a major problem due to the increase in the number of parties involved with each project. These parties include specialist consultants employed by the client and sub-contractors employed by the builder. Such increases have been brought about by the changes taking place within the building industry relating to increased design complexity, more demanding functional use of buildings, greater provision of services, more mechanisation of site work, increasing range of building materials, faster building and the current urge to sub-let all the work.

There is a direct link between the quality of information supplied to builders and their performance on site. Poor and inadequate information, increases the incidence of disputes and contractual claims whilst decreasing quality and workmanship. This usually results in the client not receiving the building on time and also the building being defective, having potential maintenance problems and the final cost escalating far beyond the original contract sum. Consultants are indirectly affected in these situations because professional indemnity insurance premiums increase as more dissatisfied clients sue for professional negligence.

The main documents to which CPI applies are drawings, specifications and bills of quantities, the production of which are controlled by the particular convention (standard procedural guideline) that has been established for each. The various documents are linked together by a Common Arrangement (CA) of coded work sections. The CA of work sections (CAWS) for building works is a document which details all work in sequential order.

It is expected that CA will have a major influence on specification writing especially when bills of quantities are not used. As SMM7 complies with the CA those producing bills need only refer to SMM7 and of course the coded specification. The coding of specifications, bills of quantities and drawings will give rise to greater consistency in data production, compatibility between documents and easier distribution of information.

The specification has greater significance within the CA as it is to be the foremost reference document for matters relating to materials and work. By applying the common arrangement to the National Building Specification (NBS) and the National Engineering Specification (NES) it is hoped that the CPI initiative will provide a standardisation of procedures nationally to increase efficiency and productivity within the building industry. Note that the NBS and NES are services available only to subscribers.

In addition, the CI/SfB *Construction Index Manual* published by the RIBA which relates to the international system for arranging project information is currently being revised to incorporate the CA. As specifications become more relevant and accurate builders are more likely to place greater emphasis on specification details although it may take time to establish confidence.

There is growing concern amongst quantity surveyors about maintaining the quality of the services they offer to clients due to the lowering of fees through competition. This could well be seen as applying dual standards when one considers that consultants have never been prepared to accept inferior quality from builders irrespective of how low a tender price is. However, with regards to quality it is likely that at some future date clients may only employ those practices that are registered by the British Standards Institution (BSI) for quality assurance. In this respect CPI may help practices gain BSI accreditation. It also follows that quality assurance accreditation may become an important factor in the selection of builders, suppliers and sub-contractors.

Builders will be affected by CPI in a number of ways. From the outset, due to the introduction of SMM7 estimators will have to revise their pricing techniques although long term benefits may be attained with the production of marginally shorter bills. By providing builders with measured quantities (for contracts with quantities), full specification information, adequate drawings and relevant preliminaries requirements estimators are expected to prepare more realistic prices. In addition to this, information for supplier and sub-contractor enquiries will be easier for builders to locate and extract.

Also builders are advised to reference their contract programmes in accordance with the CA work section codes in order to provide management with a direct link with specifications, quantities and costs. This will also help with the sequencing of both material purchase and design information. Quality control on site is likely to improve as more time is spent supervising building activity as opposed to spending time ratifying the accuracy of project information.

However, it is likely that for projects where the detailed requirements of SMM7 are considered unnecessary the Shorter Bills of Quantities method published by the Builder Group Ltd may be preferred. This method incorporates a concise standard phraseology and library of descriptions, these being produced by the authors of the original versions developed for use with full BQs prepared in accordance with SMM rules.

There are some specific changes to the measurement rules of SMM7 that builders should be aware of when preparing tenders. One important area of change which has contractual implications is that concerning general rule 10. To facilitate the use of SMM7 and take account of general rule 10 the JCT have issued amendment 7, July 1988, for use with the JCT 80 (with quantities) form of contract.

General rule 10[1] relates to the procedure for BQ production where the drawn and specification information required by these rules is not available. This rule is outlined as follows:

10.1   *Approximate quantities* – items of work which can be described and quantified in accordance with SMM7 rules for which accurate quantities cannot be ascertained shall be quantified approximately and identified as such.

Thus, the term approximate replaces the previous term provisional.

10.2   *Provisional sums* – items of work which cannot be described and quantified in accordance with the rules shall be described as provisional, stating whether it is defined or undefined

10.3   *Provisional sums defined* – this relates to work that is not completely designed but for which the following information can be given:

(a) the nature and construction of the work
(b) how and where the work is fixed to the building and what other work is fixed to it
(c) quantities which indicate the scope and extent of the work
(d) limitations on method, sequence, timing and the like as clause A35

10.4   *Provisional sums defined shall be fully accounted for in a tender* – builders are deemed to have made allowance in their tenders for this work in respect to planning, programme and the pricing of preliminaries. Such allowance is only subject to adjustment if a variation involving other measured work gives rise to adjustment

10.5   *Provisional sums undefined* – this relates to work where the information required in 10.3 cannot be given

10.6   *Provisional sums undefined shall not be fully accounted for in a tender* – builders are deemed not to have made allowance in their tenders for planning, programme and the pricing of preliminaries.

Note that in situations where the work falls within clause 10.6 it is highly probable that disputes will later arise when the parties involved try to agree the impact such work has on the production programme and in assessing the associated cost implications on preliminaries.

Amendment 7[2] not only incorporates these rules within the contract conditions but also takes account of other related matters. The main points are as follows:

Clause 2.2.2.2 is revised to include: any error in or omission of information in any item to which rule 10.3 refers shall be corrected as a variation

Clause 13.4.1.1 is revised to include: work to which rule 10.1 refers shall be measured and valued by the QS as a variation and valued in accordance with the contract valuation rules unless otherwise agreed between the parties

Clause 13.4.1.2 is revised to include: the valuation of variations to nominated work which has an approximate quantity is to be made in accordance with NSC/4 or NSC/4a provisions unless otherwise agreed between the sub-contract parties and the client

Clause 13.5.1.5 is introduced to include: where a given approximate quantity is not a reasonably* accurate forecast of the actual quantity then the bill rate shall be the basis for determining the valuation with a fair* allowance for that difference in quantity

Clause 13.5.5 is revised to include: if compliance with any variation substantially changes the conditions under which other work is executed then the changes to the other work are deemed to be a variation and so valued. Such compliance with a variation is revised to include:

- work for a provisional sum which is undefined
- work for a provisional sum which is defined where the actual work differs from that described
- work where an approximate quantity is more or less than the actual quantity.

---

* What constitutes reasonably and fair is a matter of opinion and therefore may give rise to disputes. Furthermore, the probability of such disputes arising is increased due to there being two points at which subjective judgement is required to be exercised.

Note that adjustments for the valuation of variations includes reductions as well as increases.

Another point of interest relates to relevant events for extensions of time, clause 25.4, and the list of matters which give rise to loss and/or expense. clause 26.2. For further details of this and other points reference should be made to amendment 7 and the accompanying guidance note.

Tendering trends

Building contracts There are a number of interesting trends currently developing within the industry in relation to tendering although it is not certain that such trends will continue. For instance, responses to a Contracts in Use survey[3] show an upward trend in the use of the IFC 84 together with fixed price contracts based on specifications and drawings and design and build. In addition, there is continued use of the JCT 63 though be it at a lower level than previously. By comparison, both fixed price contracts based on firm BQs and management contracts have declined in popularity.

However, traditional fixed price contracts still account for over 70% of the value of tenders included in the survey. If the figure for design and build is doubled to allow for any suggested shortfall in the value represented the traditional approach is still well over 50% of the total.

Irrespective of the popularity of the available procurement routes and associated contractual arrangements they are virtually all fixed price contracts. Only an insignificant number of contracts are based on cost reimbursement. This means that builders are usually involved in preparing detailed estimates, a very costly and time consuming activity especially if bills of quantities are not provided. Management contracting is no different as it is covertly a fixed price arrangement for the work package sub-contractors. The cost of tendering is increased for builders who are involved in competitive tendering due to the abortive costs associated with unsuccessful bids.

Builders' tendering costs Research carried out by the author,[4] involving a number of builders throughout the country, reveals that in 1985 medium sized builders on average incur proportionately lower tendering costs than do either large or small builders. In this case the majority of builders contacted report tendering costs between 0.50 and 1.00% of company turnover. However, it is surprising to find that some large builders had exceptionally high tendering costs of between 5.5 and 6.0% of turnover.

As many builders only manage to make 2 to 3% net profit per annum it is reasonable to conclude that tendering costs are significant. This conclusion is further supported by the following views from contractors:

Significance of tendering costs
60% – very significant
16% – very/quite significant
20% – quite significant
 4% – quite/not very significant.

Therefore, builders may be better seeking tendering situations which do not involve detailed cost calculations or alternatively strive to reduce tendering costs.

Turnover   The author's research also extends to include the trends in size and number of contracts for which builders were tendering. These two issues are important in that by not increasing the size (value) of jobs in line with inflation then turnover will fall in real terms. This will result in reduced profits unless the success ratio is improved and/or the number of bids is increased and/or mark-up is increased. However, increasing the number of bids is likely to result in higher tendering costs, these being abortive when bids are unsuccessful. This may also have an adverse affect on competitiveness and/or profits.

Results of the research show that relatively more medium sized builders compared to either small or large builders increased both the size and number of tenders submitted. In view of the importance of maintaining turnover to sustain profits it is surprising to find that many small and large builders did not increase the number of bids despite the fact that they were not tendering for larger jobs.

Tender price levels   The BCIS[5] have identified that building costs have increased at a higher rate than tender price levels, the gap between the two having grown steadily between 1980 and 1987. BCIS predicts that the steep increase in tender prices experienced during early 1989 will continue in 1990 and also regional variations in output are likely to be sustained. However, BCIS also predicts that the high levels of both inflation and interest rates are likely to have a dampening affect on demand in 1990.

Reduced demand is expected to result in a more stable climate for tendering towards the end of the year 1990. This fall in demand is likely to ease the problems of labour and material shortages and help reduce regional variations in tender prices. The projected forecast of both the building cost index and the tender price index, between early 1988 and late 1990, shows that the current gap between the two is likely to be maintained. These trends are based on national averages and are therefore not indicative of any regional or local market activity.

For builders in many parts of the country it appears that future tendering will remain competitive, especially as the demand for building work starts to fall. Therefore, maintaining or increasing turnover in real terms will not become easier. Costs may fall as the demand for labour falls towards the level of supply although this is likely to be discounted by builders to maintain competitiveness. In addition to this, tender prices are increasing at a higher rate than any time since 1982. Therefore, in order to maintain present levels of output, and profit, builders must obtain jobs of higher value in line with increases in either tender prices or inflation, whichever is the greater. This will inevitably put more builders under pressure.

The slow rate of increases in tender prices is generally brought about as a result of greater competition between builders when work is scarce. Here, builders must try to absorb increases in resource costs in order to maintain levels of turnover and in extreme cases to remain in business. In an attempt to absorb these costs estimators must carry out a critical review of the data used for preparing the net cost estimate in an attempt to reduce estimating inaccuracies. Note that both overpricing and underpricing can lead to problems for the builder. The former may reduce competitiveness and the latter whilst in theory maintaining competitiveness it may lead to mark-up under recovery. However, improving estimating accuracy relies heavily on accurate feedback data and prudent interpretation of same.

Any review will consider output standards of both labour and plant, quantities of materials including conversion factors and waste allowances. Alternative sequences and methods of construction must be considered to determine the most cost effective solutions. Further, alternative resources should be considered and balanced to optimise productivity. Thus, the planner must contribute to the competitiveness and efficiency of the organisation. Sub-contractors should be carefully selected based on their competitiveness, quality of work and reputation for not causing delays, not being difficult to control and not continuously seeking extra payments. The increased use of sub-contractors may also be considered to reduce the builder's risk and allow the builder take advantage of the associated credit arrangements. It is important that the most competitive prices possible are obtained whilst tendering, not after. To achieve this suppliers and sub-contractors may be prevented from submitting quotes after the contract is won.

Management also take account of the market levels and the strength of competition when determining a tender sum. Their approach to absorbing price increases is to reduce the mark-up by accepting a reduced net profit. On occasions this may involve management not including any monies for net profit and also in extreme cases could decide to reduce general overheads. The level of competition may be influenced by management due to their marketing strategy. Alternative types and size of work, alternative market sectors and regions may not be as competitive as those currently targeted.

Having won a contract it is then the responsibility of site management to implement good cost control systems in order to continue the efficiency drive. Unfortunately many builders do not operate such systems. Also, some builders that do implement cost control operate systems that are ineffective. Cost control should include all financial aspects of production including labour, materials, plant and sub-contractors. This includes: quality control to avoid defective work and materials, avoid wastage of materials and fuel when plant is idle, reducing idle time of both labour and plant, avoiding delays to subcontractors which may lead to unrecoverable daywork claims, charging sub-contractors for work carried out on their behalf, accurately valuing the work for client payments and claiming for all work to date such as variations, extras, fluctuations and loss and expense. Labour-only subcontractors may be considered for activities that are likely to be intermittently suspended due to adverse weather conditions although each time there is a lay-off there is a risk that the subcontractors may find alternative employment.

Tendering procedure

This represents the sequence of events which will lead to the builder submitting a tender, starting from the initial approach by the client to the action taken immediately after tender submission and prior to signing contracts. The Code of Estimating Practice (COEP), published by the Chartered Institute of Building, describes in detail this procedure. Whilst the contents of the publication are not mandatory the recommendations provide a basis for good practice. It must also be noted that the COEP is specifically aimed at procedures which relate to fixed price single stage selective tendering. However, much of the basic procedures and recommendations hold good irrespective of either the procurement route or the contractual arrangements in force. For example, a similar procedure to that for selecting a builder may be applied when selecting a management contractor whilst the whole tendering procedure as described in the COEP can be applied to the subsequent sub-contract packages. In addition to the COEP the Chartered Institute of Building has published COEP Supplements numbers 2 and 3 for *Design and build* and *Management contracting*, respectively.

Tendering procedure is summarised as follows:

(A) *Preselection* The consultants establish a list of suitable builders that are willing to tender and then select from the list those that will be invited to submit a tender. Preselection is therefore associated with selective tendering. In order to be considered builders should have the appropriate experience and resources for the particular project in hand. The preselection procedure includes approaching potential tenderers to determine their interest in the project. Sufficient details about the project including relevant contractual arrangements must be given to the builder at this stage in order for management to assess the extent to which the project can be accommodated in conjunction with existing commitments. The proposed date for issue of tender documents must also be provided to help with future workload considerations.

On some projects the procedure may be extended to incorporate meetings or interviews to enable the client to discuss further ideas and issues with each builder. However, on other projects the initial approach to the builder may not disclose project particulars in as much detail. Often the initial contact with the builder is by telephone especially if consultants are either familiar with the builders or when a quick response is required.

If the builder has the capacity to carry out the work and sufficient time is to be allowed for preparing a tender then the preliminary enquiry will be accepted. Where particulars of builders are not known then they are asked at this stage to prequalify. This involves builders supplying the client with particulars relating to corporate, financial and building activity status. The client may well issue a formal questionnaire about such matters for management to complete and return.

Once builders have been selected they should be notified immediately and must also be kept fully informed of any subsequent changes in the project details and arrangements. Similarly, the client should be informed immediately it becomes evident to a builder that a tender cannot be submitted. This will enable a replacement to be recruited from the original list of willing tenderers.

Note that all incoming correspondence throughout the entire contract must be date stamped to record the exact day when information, instructions, data and the like are received. It is necessary to do this with communications from all parties to ensure that the builder's interests are not compromised by future events.

(B) *Decision to tender* On receipt of the invitation and tender documents the builder must decide on whether to tender. This decision must be made as soon as possible and preferably on the first day in order to conserve time should the builder wish to tender. Where preselection has occurred the builder has in principle already agreed to tender and should only decline for legitimate reasons.

If there are no such reasons then the earlier decision must in theory be re-affirmed. This involves comparing the details provided at preselection with those received to ensure there are no significant changes which would result in declining the invitation to tender. In reality this issue is irrelevant because the decision will be based on the merits of the project as presented, as would be the case if preselection procedures had not been initiated.

When management decide to accept the invitation to tender then written confirmation must be given. A likely response could be:

> Dear Mr Jones
> *30 Grouped Flats, Wentworth Place, Bury*
> We hereby acknowledge receipt of your letter dated 20 July 19.. and confirm that a bona fide tender will be submitted in accordance with your instructions.
> Yours sincerely
>
>
> Chief estimator

In the event that the invitation is to be declined then all tender documents should be returned immediately.

(C) *Project appreciation*   As soon as management agree to submit a tender the estimator is given the tender documentation and at that point takes responsibility for the management and production of the cost estimate. Once the estimator is satisfied that all the documents have been issued then the job is given a number and entered into the tender register along with the receipt and submission date. The job may then also be entered on a Gantt chart, as shown in figure 4.1, along with other current tenders. This will provide the estimator with an instant visual statement of both tender period and submission date for each project. In addition, although the list increases frequently with the influx of new tenders this presentation makes it easy to keep track of the various submission dates. This also avoids having to sift through numerous papers and subsequent cross-referencing of data to establish which tenders are imminent. A blank construction programme may be used for this purpose if a standard chart is not available.

As well as updating the tender chart it is also advisable, as an additional reminder, to write the tender submission date clearly on the front of the bill or schedule. This is of particular importance if a

TENDER SUBMISSIONS		Year(s)												
Project	Month	March				April				May				Ju
	Week	1	2	3	4	1	2	3	4	1	2	3	4	1
factory units, Hull			/-----/24th March											
5 storey office block, Leeds						/---------/27th April								
Sports complex, York						/--------/30th April								
Alterations to flats, Batley								/-----/26th April						

Figure 4.1   Tender chart

time deadline is stipulated which may be 11 am, 12 noon or first post. Tenders will normally be rejected by the client if not received on or before the stated deadline.

One other preliminary organisational task to be performed by the estimator is to prepare a tender timetable for the project. This identifies the activities that need to be performed, with key dates, in order to submit a tender on time. Figure 4.2 shows the likely format of a tender timetable where bills of quantities are provided and each stage of the tendering procedure to which the activities relate is identified by the letters in the right hand column. If bills are not provided or arrangements require the builder to produce other documentation including design details then the associated activities must be appropriately programmed within the tender period.

The tender period in figure 4.2 is determined by the date when documents are received and the date when tenders must be submitted. All activities must be programmed between these dates. If tender documents are received prior to Christmas then an extension to the tender period should be requested. This is because the building industry, apart from consultants, shuts down for two weeks and therefore quotations cannot be obtained. Starting at the beginning of the timetable the decision to tender is programmed to take place on day one. This is immediately followed by the period for abstracting and posting data for suppliers and sub-contractors. The time allowed here is usually three to four days. The next step is to programme events in reverse order from the end of the timetable. The submission time is then allocated to the programme followed by the period for adjudication which will be half a day. The tender report is then programmed followed by the report, reconciliation and extensions. Half a day has been allowed for extending the bill on the basis that the activity will be sub-contracted out. Sub-contracting saves time and provides greater accuracy. Some builders may opt to carry out the extensions

JOB:						Month									
date	1	3	5	7	9	11	13	15	17	19	21	23	25	27	29	31
day	M	W	F	M	W	F	M	W	F	M	W	F	M	W	F	M
Decision to tender	—															B
Process enquiries		——					*			**						C
Visit site and consultant			—													C
Sequence and method			—							·						C
Price measured work(estimating)					————————											D
Arithmetic extensions												—				D
Price site overheads													———			E
Reconciliation with planning data														—		E
Tender report														—		E
Adjudication															—	F
Tender submission															—	F

```
    * Latest date for receipt of quotes from suppliers
   ** Latest date for receipt of quotes from sub-contractors
```

Figure 4.2   Tender activity timetable

during the estimating period using junior staff. When these stages have been programmed then the remaining tasks are allocated to the timetable.

Once the preliminary tasks are complete the estimating activity begins. At this stage a comprehensive examination of the tender documents is carried out by the estimator in order to familiarise himself with the project, identifying the scope of work for pricing and planning purposes. The proportions of work to be carried out by the builder and sub-contractors is established along with an outline of the likely construction programme and methods. As the construction sequence, durations and methods influence the way in which the work is priced it is important that these details are finalised for use when estimating. Note that alternative methods are likely to influence the construction programme and therefore any associated preliminaries costs. The estimator or buyer must also comb the bill and abstract data relating to all work and materials for which prices must be obtained, the information being subsequently dispatched to sub-contractors and suppliers.

In addition to the planning information the estimator and planner must visit the site and report on matters concerning the site: access, services, ground conditions, parking restrictions, location with regard to suppliers, local tips, availability of labour, public transport, other sites that may compete for labour, potential vandalism, noise, etc. Problems associated with such matters along with queries on construction and sequence arising from the specification and drawings may then be raised with the architect during the visit to his office. It is normal practice to visit the architect to view all the complete set of design drawings as usually only a limited number of drawings are issued for tendering purposes.

(D) *Price the measured work*   This initially involves establishing the cost of employing the operatives that will be engaged on site and checking the validity of quotations from suppliers and sub-contractors as they are received. Once quotations are checked the estimator decides on which are to be used for pricing the work. The cost of each item is calculated and grouped with other costs to provide a total sum. As all quotes are not returned at the same time the estimating process is fragmented. However, whilst waiting for quotes the estimator may price sundry items in full and other items in part or alternatively price other tenders for which quotes have been received. Often due to this arrangement single items that cannot be priced can be lost amongst items that have been priced. To avoid the possibility of missing such items and avoid the need for numerous detailed checks it is advisable to flag such items by attaching a paper clip to the relevant page and also lightly pencil in a cross alongside the unpriced item.

Once deadlines for return of quotes is exceeded then the chasing commences. This involves constantly telephoning the various suppliers and sub-contractors to coax them into providing the information required. When the system of flagging has been adopted then the need to debrief the person responsible for chasing the quotes is virtually eliminated. The terms and conditions, discounts, etc, must be established for all verbal quotations otherwise the prices are meaningless. At the time the verbal quote is received the builder must request that written confirmation is provided. In the event that some prices cannot be obtained prior to tender submission then the estimator must use judgement to make appropriate cost allowances.

A list should be kept of any queries arising from the tender documents such as incorrect unit of measurement, insufficient quantity or conflicting information shown on drawings. The architect is informed of the queries, normally by telephone, at an appropriate time. The architect must answer the queries in writing as soon as possible and such details must be issued to all tenderers if it involves amending tender documents. Queries from other builders must be dealt with likewise. This procedure must be complied with to ensure that none of the tenderers can gain an unfair advantage over the others.

(E) *Completing the cost estimate*　Additions to any PC sums and daywork are completed and then the project overheads are priced. If the builder is required to submit a firm price tender then any allowances relating to this may be dealt with here as a global assessment or earlier during the pricing of individual bill items.

On completion, the estimate should be reviewed to ensure that all the work has been priced and there are no obvious errors. A cash flow forecast for the project is then prepared by either the estimator, surveyor or planner. An appraisal of the potential profitability of the project may then take place with the aid of statistics from previous jobs of a similar nature. Reconciliation with data produced by the planner also takes place to check that the selected construction methods are the most appropriate. Here the estimate is evaluated to ensure that it is a realistic financial representation of the likely cost of carrying out the work.

When the estimator has all the information for management to consider then it must be processed for submission to management in the form of a report. The report is concise, giving specific details relating to the project including an analysis of the net cost estimate, conditions of contract, construction methods, project overheads, problems or points of concern, cash flow, retention percentage and other financial matters, other tenderers and a summary of previous bidding performance on similar work. Tender documents, programme and other relevant information such as late quotations are attached to the report.

(F) *Tender finalisation*　The tender sum is determined by management at the adjudication meeting after all the relevant facts concerning the project have been considered. The estimator, planner, surveyor, contracts manager and others involved with the preparation of the tender attend the meeting to discuss points of issue with management. Management therefore decide on the level of overheads and profit that is to be added to the net cost estimate. If they decide that specific prices contained in the estimate are to be changed or that the overheads and profit are to be added in a particular manner then precise instructions should be given. The latter point initially relates to tender submissions that involve builders providing a detailed cost breakdown of the bid. Where a detailed cost breakdown is not required then the distribution of costs would only concern the successful tenderer.

The completed form of tender is signed by the builder and then returned to the client in the envelope provided. It is usual for record purposes to take a copy of the signed tender form prior to submission. If other documents or data are to be submitted along with the form of tender then the estimator must ensure they are all included in the submission.

(G) *Action after tender*   All recorded data concerning the project must be placed in an envelope for filing and the value of the tender recorded in the tender register. The client will in due course inform builders of the bidding results. The result is also recorded in the tender register. When the full list of bids and bidders (the former in rank order, the latter in alphabetic order) is received then the estimator will assess tender performance. This involves establishing the levels of competition by calculating the percentage differences in bids.

If a bid is successful then relevant information from the tender file will be circulated to those responsible for managing the building work. During the building period the estimator should acquaint himself with actual site performance which together with a reconciliation of estimated and actual costs, as parts of the work are completed, should provide feedback for future estimates.

Alterations and refurbishment   Because of the specialist nature of alteration and refurbishment work in 1987 the CIOB published a code of estimating practice supplement, number one, entitled *Refurbishment and modernisation.* In comparison with new work tendering for refurbishment work is much more difficult. Because of the high volume of refurbishment work carried out at present some of the associated estimating problems are outlined as follows:

Working restrictions

Working whilst the building is occupied – this may require provision of dust and security screens for work in banks and building societies, daily clearing away of debris and sweeping floors, moving furniture and involve piecemeal working by operatives. Noise restrictions may hinder demolition work and, as is the case with hospital contracts, the architect may have the power to suspend the work at any time.

Access

Restrictions may be imposed by the police regarding footpath obstruction and restricted loading/unloading periods. Note that these may apply equally to new work on confined sites. Double handling of debris and contract materials is usually a problem especially when work is at the rear of the building via narrow alley ways or with high rise buildings where lifts are not available to the builder. Double handling is usually dealt with separately, an assessment of weekly manpower requirements produced for such activity.

Access to certain parts of the building may only be permitted on completion of work in other areas which is a covert form of phasing the work. Removal of debris may be achieved by providing shoots from windows which discharge directly into lorries or skips. An alternative but more costly method is to load the debris into containers and manhandle them out of the building.

Specification

Where the tender documents include drawings and a specification the drawings may be incorrectly dimensioned or conflict with details contained in the specification. Problems which generally arise whilst the work is being carried out, when it is too late for the builder to alter his price, relate to the size of openings being too small for certain materials to pass through. This often occurs when specified cold water storage tanks are larger than the existing loft accesses or hot water cylinders are larger than the cylinder cupboard door openings.

Builders are often unrealistically expected to foresee such problems that are so often overlooked (or may be not!) by those responsible for designing the work. Note that during one particular contract a builder was told that he should have allowed for demolishing and rebuilding a wall and make good finishes to allow access for an industrial central heating boiler, details of which were not given at the time of tender.

Extent of work required

Descriptions such as *Hack Off* plaster where loose and *Make Good* plaster cracks are also inadequate. The actual amount of plaster to take down and make good is only realised when work commences. With regards to plaster cracks it is impossible to assess when concealed by existing wallpaper as is usually the case. Further, should the estimator instruct the plasterer to quote for chasing out the wall and replastering or merely trowel plaster into the crack and hope that it will be adequate.

Another ambiguous requirement generally incorporated within the description of forming openings in walls is that of making good finishings. It is not certain as to whether this refers to paintwork or wallpaper to walls. If the paintwork is to be made good is the making good limited to the surface of the new plaster or is the whole wall required to be repainted?

Pricing the work

Many items are unique and therefore have to be priced on merit during a site visit. This relies heavily on the estimators experience of pricing refurbishment work. Forming openings in walls may be considered a repetitive operation for any project. However, this is not the case as brick and mortar strengths vary as does deterioration of the materials. Thus, it may take six or eight times as long to cut out openings in walls built of engineering bricks such as those to bank vaults as opposed to walls in similar condition built with common bricks.

Raking out joints of brickwork for later repointing is much faster by sthill saw than by hand although this creates an excessive amount of dust. Note that there are likely to be part load charges for many items required in small quantities due to both the nature of the work and possible lack of storage facilities on site.

Risk

The work on site is easily disrupted due to variations although the extent of such disruption is difficult to quantify. Thus, reimbursement for loss and expense due to disruption of the works becomes very difficult to assess and substantiate. The builder is usually offered a random 10 or 15% extra payment as compensation in virtually every situation. However, unless realistic assessments are made the builder's financial risk becomes even greater than that arising from the estimating problems described earlier.

References

1 RICS, and BEC, *Standard method of measurement of building works* – General rule 10, seventh edition, RICS and BEC 1988, pp 14.
2 JCT, *Standard form of building contract*, 1980 edition: Amendment 7, RIBA 1988.
3 RICS Junior Organisation, 'Survey – Contracts in use', *CQS*, January 1989, pp 24–26.
4 COOK, AE, An analysis of the cost of preparing tenders for fixed price contracts to determine the worth of such procedures, CIOB, Technical information service, no. 120, 199 –,   pp 4–5.
5 BCIS *News*, no. 24, RICS 1988.

Questions

1 Many contractors make a detailed assessment of the resources required for a project in order to produce accurate rates for the bills of quantities. At the same time they are often aware of the client's budget and the strength of competition.

   Discuss how these factors influence contractors' tenders.

2 Consider the aims and effectiveness of recent attempts to develop methods for producing shorter bills of quantities.

3 Explain why the accurate pricing of maintenance and repair work, to give a realistic quotation, is more difficult than estimating for measured new work.

4 Identify the role of the specification in project documentation and explain how this role might change with the introduction of SMM7 and the proposed co-ordinated approach to project information (CPI).

5 Contractors' Own Work

Scope of direct building work

Building work The direct building work comprises that which represents the finished building including external works and drainage but excluding PC sums, provisional sums and preliminary items. Direct work may be made up entirely of new build or alterations or a mixture of both. This information should be accurately represented in the tender bills and drawings or in the drawings and specification where bills are not used. Where BQs are used the direct work is represented by the measured work section.

Part of the work will be carried out by the builder and the remainder by sub-contractors. The extent to which traditional builders' work is sub-let varies between organisations. The builder's estimator is involved in estimating from first principles, using analytical and operational estimating techniques, all the work that is to be undertaken directly by the builder. In this respect the builder is involved with the five Ms, these being *men*, *materials*, *machines*, *money* and *management*.

Supplementary items Whilst most items to be priced represent the finished building there are a number of items, such as protection and general plant items, that do not. These supplementary items are included for the convenience of builders to enable them to separate incidental costs if so desired. This avoids having to distribute supplementary costs throughout a large number of associated work items – which would have to be first identified. Further, this approach does not disrupt or compromise the pricing of the measured work items.

The decision to price protection items and the extent to which they are priced varies between jobs. For example, should brickwork be protected to ensure work can continue in adverse weather conditions and if so then what form of protection is to be provided? Such problems also occur with pre-finished doors, hardwood floor coverings, hardwood doors and frames, stone cills, sanitary ware and the like. The need for protection commences immediately upon delivery to site and continues during storage, distribution, fixing and whilst in situ until such times as the works are handed over to the client.

Resources employed

Net cost unit rates are established using three resources, namely *labour*, *materials* and *plant*. A combination of these are often used as many items do not involve all three.

Labour The two categories of labour are skilled and semi skilled, the difference being the ability of joiners, bricklayers and steel fixers as opposed to that of general labourers. The basic minimum weekly rates of pay for building operatives and apprentices in England, Wales and Scotland are determined annually by the National Joint Council for the Building Industry (NJCBI). Operatives employed in both London and Liverpool are paid marginally more.

All operatives are entitled to extra payments over and above the basic wage for both additional responsibility and extra skill such as trades chargehands, gangers and mechanical plant operators, scaffolders and drain layers. These and other entitlements such as lodging and travel allowances and enhanced rates for overtime, shift work and working in difficult conditions are all contained in the NJCBI Working Rule Agreement.

The labour content of all prices is based on an all-in hourly rate. This is an average cost of employing an operative (direct labour) during normal working hours, currently thirty nine hours per week from Monday to Friday, based on the operatives wages plus the builder's contributions as an employer. The all-in hourly rate is derived by calculating the total annual cost of employing an operative and dividing the total by the number of hours that the operative will work. If required the calculation may be split into winter and summer for easier assessment of overtime payments during the summer months when sites are open longer. An example of this method is detailed in the COEP published by the CIOB.

As there are wage differentials in each locality, and often more than the minimum, it is necessary for the estimator to establish the prevailing wage levels of operatives for each project. Thus, new all-in hourly labour rates must be calculated for every tender.

To price each work item the estimator must allocate one or more operatives to the task and allot times (hours) against them. Output standards (labour constants) are commonly used for this purpose although may need adjustment in specific cases. These are set times based on an average performance of operatives of varying ability recorded over a range of suitable projects.

Thus, given an output standard of 12 hours per cubic metre for carcassing timber and an all-in hourly rate of £5 then the labour cost per metre for fixing a 25 mm × 75 mm section of timber would be:

Time = 12 × .025 × .075 = .023 hrs/m
Labour cost = .023 × £5 = £0.12/m.

Output standards for work such as brickwork or blockwork are more appropriately derived by assessing the number of bricks or blocks likely to be laid per hour together with the selected gang size (ratio of bricklayers to hod carriers). The time per square metre of walling can then be calculated for both craftsman and labourer. Note that whilst the estimator establishes the labour cost using two different rates bricklaying gangs that continually work together, as within a gang they all work at the same speed, divide the weekly earnings equally.

Note that where plant output dominates an item, such as a banksman working alongside excavators the labour time is determined by the speed of the machines.

Materials   The units of measurement often differ from the units of purchase, for example aggregates such as limestone, sand and broken brick are bought per tonne whereas they are measured and costed either per square metre or cubic metre. Also bricks are bought per thousand (unless specials) although costed per square metre. Many material prices have therefore to be converted to the appropriate unit by the estimator. The two examples given are easy to deal with using standard conversion factors:

limestone – weight per cubic metre = 2 tonnes
Thus at £8/tonne the cost of material = £16/m³

If the limestone is measured square metres average 125 mm depth then the cost of material = .125 × £16 = £2/m²

bricks – number per square metre per half brick wall = 60.
Thus at £92/1000 the cost of material = $\frac{£92}{1000}$ × 60

= £5.52/m²

Carcassing timber poses a different problem in that supplier **A** may quote per cubic metre and supplier **B** may quote per 100 linear metres. The estimator must in such circumstances determine which of the two is the more competitive price by converting one quotation into the same unit as the other.

Thus if for 25 mm × 50 mm timber **A**'s price is £197/m³ and **B**'s price is £25.90/100 m to determine the lowest offer
Conversion of **B**'s price = $\frac{£25.90}{100 \text{ m} \times .025 \times .05}$ = £207.20/m³
Offer **A** is therefore the lowest.

Many other materials are measured as the net area laid although the fixing method involves lapping as in the case of mesh fabric reinforcement, damp proof courses and tongued and grooved boarding. Rather than alter the net area measured the estimator must increase the price of the material to take account of the shortfall caused by such laps:

Thus if mesh reinforcement costs £1.62/m², sheet size is 2.40 m × 4.80 m and given laps are 200 mm at sides and 300 mm at ends to determine the price per square metre inclusive of lapped material:

Sheet area = 2.40 m × 4.80 m = 11.52 m²
Effective area per sheet = (2400 − 200) (4800 − 300)
= 9.90 m²
Area of laps = 11.52 − 9.90 = 1.62 m²
Percentage increase required = $\frac{1.62}{9.90}$ × 100% = 16.4%

The adjusted price of reinforcement = £1.62 × 116.4%
= £1.89/m².

Waste allowances and offloading costs need to be added to all materials. Waste allowances obviously vary on each job, between each organisation and between trades. Whilst an average allowance may be applied to many materials those of great value and those susceptible to damage need to be considered more carefully.

One other point to consider is that of delivery arrangements. Where certain sundry materials are to be required by site in small quantities then collection by the builder may be considered. When it is inconvenient or not feasible to collect materials then small load requirements are likely to be charged at higher rate than those quoted for full loads. This is to cover the suppliers haulage costs which are usually significant in relation to the value of goods, especially where long distance haulage is involved.

Where part load charges may be likely with pre-mixed concrete, to avoid such charges it may be worth considering phasing small pours to coincide with larger pours. Alternatively, if a stronger mix is required in full loads then use the stronger mix in lieu of the weaker mix, the cost difference being much less than part load charges. Many builders have storage facilities at their offices and are therefore able to obtain certain goods in large quantities for intermittent distribution of small quantities to individual sites within the locality as required. Cement, wheelbarrows, nails, screws and the like may be dealt with this way.

Plant The two categories of plant are mechanical and non-mechanical. Non-mechanical plant such as tarpaulins, ladders, barrows, buckets and the like are purchased by builders and replaced as and when necessary. As these may be used on numerous jobs at various times it is more convenient to include the cost of such items, based on a percentage of company turnover, in either the preliminaries or the general overheads. Note that general scaffolding, formwork props and the like whilst being non-mechanical are normally dealt with separately due to the specific requirements of each project.

On occasions special equipment may have to be obtained for a specific purpose although not likely to be used for other contracts. In such cases the builder may either hire or buy the equipment, the full cost of which must be included in the estimate.

Mechanical plant includes lorries, hydraulic excavators/loaders, cranes, dumpers, mortar mixers, electric drills and transformers, pumps, hoists, vibrators and the like. The cost of such equipment may be included in the unit rates or in the preliminaries as a lump sum for all plant. Where items of plant are serving numerous trades it is usually more convenient not to try and distribute the cost within the unit rates. However, unit rates for certain work items, such as excavation and disposal, mainly consist of plant costs therefore it would be inappropriate to include the cost of these plant items in the preliminaries.

Plant costs for each work item are established by applying plant output standards to an all-in hourly rate for plant in a similar way to that adopted for labour. However, for activities where labour output dictates time then the plant adopts the duration of the activity. Thus, where concrete is mixed on site the operation is regulated by the output of the slowest resource, either the mixing plant or the transport or the concrete gang, depending on the resources selected. The all-in hourly rate for each item of plant is an average cost per hour including driver or operator where applicable and for petrol or diesel driven plant is inclusive of fuel, oil and lubricating grease.

Depending on whether the plant is hired or owned the all-in hourly rate will be as quoted by the hire company or determined by the builder respectively. When dealing with hired plant consideration must also be given to minimum hire periods when plant is only required for short periods. Note that lorries and excavators/loaders are usually hired with drivers and mortar mixers required for brickwork and blockwork are normally operated by the bricklayers' labourer.

As plant is often standing idle (down time) outputs derived from first principles using manufacturer's data should be adjusted to take account of anticipated standing time. The extent to which plant will be utilised does vary although a 60% utilisation factor should be adequate for general earthwork operations. Schedules of output standards should always be prepared with direct reference to the specific size(s) of plant to which the data relates. This will eliminate the need for random selection of output standards. For example, there are a number of different bucket sizes available for use with hydraulic excavators, each providing a different output. Thus, to dig a trench 600 mm wide an appropriate backhoe bucket width which is narrower than the trench width must be selected. This is demonstrated in figure 5.1.

```
------------------------------------------------------------------
    JCB 3CX backhoe loader

    Bucket width      (mm)      305    400    457    610

    Bucket capacity   (m3)      0.06   0.09   0.12   0.17

    (Manufacturer's data)
------------------------------------------------------------------
    Output
    Assume 1 minute* to fill
    each bucket (cycle) and
    bucket is heaped to
    account for earth
    bulking           (m3/hr)          5.40

    Output with 60%
    utilisation factor (m3/hr)         3.24
------------------------------------------------------------------
    Unit time         (hrs/m3)         0.31
------------------------------------------------------------------
```

* This cycle is for excavations not exceeding 1 m depth. The lift and dip time components of the cycle should be increased when excavating to greater depths.

Figure 5.1   Calculation of output standard for excavator

In addition to the all-in hourly plant rate other costs that are incurred must be determined and included in the estimate. Such additional costs may include transporting to and from site, erecting and dismantling, commissioning, providing three-phase power supply and hard standings for such plant as tower cranes, drivers/ operators and for tax and insurance if to be driven on public highways. Apart from the provision of drivers/operators these are fixed costs which are very significant in circumstances where items of plant are required for short periods.

As soon as an item of plant has completed the task(s) in hand it should be taken off site, especially if it is hired. Many site agents hold plant on hire for several weeks on the basis that it will be required for a future operation. This is a very uneconomical way to manage plant and should not be allowed to continue in any organisation.

Plant acquisition   Builders have the option to purchase, lease or hire the plant they require. Small builders tend not to own much plant beyond such items as a mixer, van or small lorry, depending on the type of work with which they are mainly involved. The requirements of larger builders are usually more extensive due to both the diversity and the volume of work undertaken. As plant is costly to purchase and maintain, detailed cost benefit appraisals need to be undertaken before any orgnisation is committed to any large capital investment.

The decision to purchase an item of plant rather than hire from a plant hire company may be made due to one of the following reasons:

to meet future workload requirements – here the plant is likely to have a high level of utilisation. The plant may in fact be required to replace existing equipment

to meet the requirements of one specific contract – here the contract is of sufficient size and value as to enable the plant to be written off on the job whilst still maintaining cost effectiveness

to use short term and hire to others long term – here the plant is neither required for future workload requirements nor written off on one particular contract. Once the needs of the builder are fulfilled the plant is transferred to the plant hire section within the organisation.

Financial advantages of buying:

- purchasing near the end of the financial year to reduce taxable profit
- boosting the organisation's balance sheet
- taking advantage of tax relief on loan interest or other tax concessions which can be spread over a period up to five years
- owning a capital asset once costs and profit requirements have been recovered. The plant may then be sold, value depending on demand, or employed on subsequent contracts at reduced rates to increase competitiveness when tendering
- providing plant more economically than that offered by hire companies as one tier of overheads and profit is eliminated.

However, plant hire is still very popular amongst builders because of the flexibility of the arrangement especially during periods of recession within the industry. This option also eliminates the need for costly maintenance, a commitment which increases with the life of the plant. Some plant hire companies are subsidiaries of building organisations. Whilst such affiliations exists the hire companies must achieve their own set profit targets. Therefore, plant is hired out to the parent organisation at the same commercial rates as those offered to the parent company's competitors.

Domestic sub-contractors   To complete the pricing of the direct builder's work the estimator must include quotations received for work which is to be sub-let. At the tender stage in addition to the total price for their work sub-contractors may provide a page by page or unit rate breakdown, the latter being preferred by the builder's estimator especially where only parts of the enquiry have been priced or where a priced BQ has to be submitted to the client together with the form of tender.

However, whilst some sub-contractors prepare net cost estimates based on unit rate estimating, many prefer to establish their estimates based on lump sums for labour, material and plant costs for the job as a whole or broken down into convenient sections or activities. As this pricing format differs to that normally required by builders for entering rates into a BQ the sub-contractor's estimate has to be converted. Problems that arise from this practice include:

- delays in converting lump sums into unit rates
- difficulties with distributing lump sums throughout a number items, in the form of unit rates, in such a manner as to obtain a true cost representation of each
- policy of providing a unit rate breakdown to only the successful builder
- policy of only providing the data if the successful builder intends to place an order with the sub-contractor
- inappropriate distribution of costs may lead to further problems during the contract when agreeing variation accounts.

Having selected the quotations that are to be incorporated into the builder's estimate and all necessary price adjustments are completed such unit rates or lump sums are entered in the appropriate section of the estimate. Some quotations may been obtained from sub-contractors for work which the builder's operatives are able to perform. This approach may be adopted when either specific operatives are in short supply or a sub-contractor can offer either better quality and efficiency at a more economical cost. In such circumstances the estimator would price the work at the builder's rates and then compare his price with those of the sub-contractors before deciding which rates to include in the estimate.

In addition to this the estimator may occasionally have to estimate the cost of certain specialist work when quotations for specific work have not been received. This may prove difficult when tendering on drawings and specification for such installations as heating and electrical as builder's estimators are not accustomed to estimating the work. Further, in such circumstances there would be little time left to prepare detailed estimates for such work. Here, it may be possible to attempt to locate a sub-contractor, not on the enquiry list, who has quoted for a competitor. If this is unsuccessful then try to obtain a cost guide from other sub-contractor sources.

Question
Building contractors are sometimes reluctant, at the tender stage, to rely on sub-contractors' prices for in situ elements of the structure and fabric. However, these portions of the work are often sub-let during construction.
Discuss.

6 The Collection of Price Data

Suppliers and sub-contractors

Types of suppliers and sub-contractors   Estimators obtain prices for materials and sub-let work from the various suppliers and sub-contractors that trade within the industry in order to produce net cost estimates for each tender. These organisations are referred to as domestic suppliers and sub-contractors. They are distinct from nominated or named organisations for two reasons. The first being that the main contract only recognises the existence of the builder, not the builder's suppliers and sub-contractors, notwithstanding the fact that the architect must approve the appointment of all domestic sub-contractors. The second being that the builder is free to choose which domestic organisations he wishes to trade with.

With nomination the architect stipulates which organisations the builder must enter into contracts with. Here, the architect is responsible for selecting competent organisations and obtaining suitable quotations from them.

Named suppliers and sub-contractors are used with the JCT IFC 84 form of contract in lieu of nominations. However, in the past naming has been used with JCT 63 forms of contract together with nomination. Naming is to some extent part nominated and part domestic. They are nominated to the extent that the builder is restricted to using the organisation named by the architect in either the tender documents or an architects' instruction. Note that neither the client nor the architect accept any liability for the competence of such organisations, therefore the builder is presented with a fait accompli. Naming is similar to domestic in that it is part of the builder's direct work but the builder does not have a choice as to which organisation to select.

In most instances sub-contractors provide all the labour, materials and specialist plant necessary to carry out their work. This distinguishes them from labour-only sub-contractors. Labour-only sub-contractors are provided with the necessary materials by the builder. Some labour-only sub-contractors may be self employed individuals hired on site or through an agency whilst others are organisations that employ a number of operatives who's skills are contracted out to builders. Note that operatives employed by a labour-only organisation may be self-employed.

The Building Employers Confederation (BEC) has produced a labour-only sub-contract form of agreement for main contractors. There are two points of particular interest within this document which relate to payments to the sub-contractor. The first is the provision, under the special conditions section and G1 together with G3 of the general conditions, for establishing the level of retention to be held on payments. The second under G1 entitles the sub-contractor to weekly payments. Note that it is more likely that labour-only organisations as opposed to individual operatives would enter into such formal agreements. Whilst the use of the BEC or any alternative agreement is not mandatory it is recommended that they are used whenever possible.

It is not always possible at the tender stage to obtain quotations from labour-only sub-contracting organisations. Further, quotations cannot be obtained from either an employment agency or an individual. This is because agencies only offer operatives on an hourly basis and individuals offer their services as the building work is proceeding. Therefore, it is most likely that the estimator will have priced such work at tender stage.

An outline of the financial implications for a builder which arise from the use of both domestic and nominated sub-contractors is displayed in figure 6.1.

	Nominated	Domestic	Labour-only
Tender price:	value stated plus contractor additions	quotation plus contractor additions	builder's estimated price (or quotation)
Risk:	limited	all*	all*
Finance:	none	usually none	all (unless monthly payments can be agreed
Profit:	proportional to final account value	fixed (unless variations occur	established when prices are agreed (fixed if quoted at tender)

* Whilst all the risk ultimately remains with the builder as opposed to the client under the main contract the risk is covertly passed on to the sub-contractor.

Figure 6.1   Financial implications for a builder when employing different types of sub-contractors

Selection Builders maintain records of suitable suppliers and sub-contractors in the same way that consultants keep approved lists of builders. Details of past and current performance are monitored and adjusted constantly to provide up-to-date information for tendering purposes.

Further, in the case of sub-contractors, details are also kept of size and value of work undertaken together with the regions within which they operate. Whilst these records are the main source of reference when preparing lists of organisations from which to obtain quotations others may also be invited to quote. This may occur due to either the inclusion of named organisations or when tendering in a new location or to provide opportunities for other organisations to demonstrate their ability.

The final selection for inclusion in the net cost estimate takes place when all quotations relating to each material or specialist work categories are received. Quotations are checked, noting the terms and conditions and then compared with like quotations to determine those which are to be used.

Enquiries Enquiries may be have to be informal when the builder is given little time to submit a tender. In these circumstances many prices are obtained by telephone. When prices are offered in this manner it is important that they be accompanied by details of relevant discounts and periods for which firm price applies. Further, all verbal quotations must be confirmed in writing by the specific suppliers and sub-contractors. For certain materials and work where it is necessary for those quoting to have detailed information this may be delivered and later collected by hand.

If such information can only be made available nearer the end of the tender period it will be necessary to contact individual organisations immediately for the purpose of persuading them to agree to the speedy pricing of the work at short notice. This is one of the many occasions it benefits builders who maintain good relationships with those they trade.

When an adequate tender period is given then details of all items for which the builder requires a price should be issued in writing to all suppliers, plant hire firms and sub-contractors. These details must be accompanied by the terms and conditions of the enquiry and any other necessary information. The object of this process is to obtain accurate competitive quotations from these organisations. Enquiries should therefore contain information as detailed in table 6.1.

Where provided as a tender document a BQ is an important source of readily available information as it contains most of the information necessary for the builder to prepare enquiries. However, the usefulness of information contained in BQs prepared by

Data	Suppliers	Sub-contractors
Name and address of project	YES	YES
Names of employer and consultants	NO	YES
Materials specification	YES	YES
Description of materials/work (with extracts from BQs and drawings where appropriate)	YES	YES
Relevant details of main contract and sub-contract conditions	NO	YES
Firm or fluctuating* price	YES**	YES
Access details/restrictions	YES	YES
Site plant, storage facilities and industrial relations policy	NO	YES
Delivery programme, part loads, special requirements such as crane off-load bricks on pallets	YES	NO
Programme of the works including that of sub-contractors, method statement, details of phasing	NO	YES
Required discounts	YES	YES
Where further details and drawings may be inspected	NO	YES
Request that all items on extensive delivery be detailed	YES	NO
Daywork: %age additions to prime cost are required to be submitted with quote	NO	YES
Services or attendances to be provided by the builder are to be included in the quote	NO	YES
Date by which quote must be received	YES	YES
Period for which the quotation remains open for acceptance	YES	YES
Checklist of all information issued	YES	YES

* Where fluctuations apply details of the method of adjustment must be given. A list of labour and material basic prices must be obtained from sub-contractors if the adjustment is to be based on actual changes in such prices.

** It is highly improbable that suppliers will offer a firm price quotation. Further, quotations from suppliers are submitted on the basis that all materials supplied will be charged at the prices current at the time of delivery.

Table 6.1   Contents of material and sub-contract enquiries

builders varies with the level of accuracy and detail by which they are prepared. Here, approximate quantities are usually prepared and this fact would have to be conveyed to those quoting. The information contained within such a document would generally be confined to quantification of the work. Specification and contract details would therefore be obtained from the tender documents provided by the client.

The procedure for preparing enquiries commences with the extraction of information from the BQ. This involves working systematically through the document and recording on separate sheets all the relevant parts of the BQ that will be required by those quoting. The estimator or buyer will acquaint himself with the contents of the BQ prior to extracting any information. Once familiar with the contents of the BQ experienced staff are capable of extracting most of the required information from one interrogation of the BQ. This is achieved by recording all the information for the different material and sub-contract enquiries as it arises. Thus, details of relevant preliminary, preamble and measured work sections are developed as the process advances. To facilitate this individual enquiry sheets, as shown by figure 6.2, are devoted to each material or sub-contract types such as woodwork, ironmongery, general building materials, roof tiling, glazing and plumbing. Note that the enquiry sheet featured not only combines material and sub-contract data but also incorporates both the issue and receipt stages of the process. Where drawings are issued as part of the information provided, these may also be entered on the enquiry sheet. Whilst many builders deal with each of these four aspects on separate sets of sheets the use of combined sheets reduces the total number necessary. Once the enquiries have been issued the materials sheets are separated from the sub-contract sheets.

The method of recording details of all specialist work and many materials is by page reference as shown in figure 6.2. However, materials such as bricks, wall ties, dpcs and the like are not presented in an appropriate format for pricing by suppliers. Further, some materials are dispersed throughout the bill, for example pre-mixed concrete is usually found in the substructure, superstructure and external works sections. The quantities for these materials must therefore be calculated from the bill items for inclusion on the enquiry sheet:

Bricks/blocks		*Concrete*
Commons	5000 number	1:3:6 mix 50 m^3
Facings	16000 number	1:2:4 mix 110 m^3
Birdsmouth specials	800	
100 mm blocks	700 m^2	
150 mm blocks	120 m^2	

```
Enquiry for project ..........

Materials enquiry  ☐           Sub-contract enquiry  ☐

Description of materials/trade ........................

Latest return date .......
```

Details of the enquiry/Bill references (Bill/Page/Item ref)		
1/2/C-E, H	3/43/A-L, R-T	
1/6/ALL		
2/5/ALL		
2/6/A-J		
3/42/H-K		

INTERNAL USE ONLY				
List of tenderers	Issue date	Returned date	Price	Lowest
1				
2				
3				
4				

Required number of copies of enquiry details ☐

Figure 6.2   Enquiry sheet

These lists can then be typed and checked ready for dispatch.

Having completed all the enquiry sheets the next task is to photocopy all the bill pages in sufficient quantities to meet the needs of all suppliers and sub-contractors.

First, the number of copies required off each bill page must be established. This is achieved by analysing the bill references contained on the enquiry sheets, from which cumulative lists are prepared. The total for any particular bill page is the sum of the numbers, indicated in the box at the bottom of each sheet, on all the sheets which contain that page reference. These collectively form the tender photocopying schedule.

Second, it is necessary to work through the bill starting at the front and each page is photocopied, the number of copies being as shown on the photocopying schedule. This task is usually given to an office junior to perform. Whilst the copies are being produced the enquiry sheets should be given to the typist, along with an address book, to prepare enquiry letters or forms and to address envelopes. Note that if envelopes of different sizes are required the typist must be informed.

Once the photocopying is complete it is collated in accordance with details on the enquiry sheets. Where only parts of pages are applicable then superfluous parts are deleted in ink. The information relating to each enquiry is then attached to a letter of enquiry, drawings, programme, etc, where necessary and then dispatched in the relevant envelope. If the enquiry letter does not contain a checklist of items to be priced then a photocopy of the upper part of the respective enquiry sheet can be enclosed. It is important that this process is well managed to ensure that full details are dispatched to the correct destinations.

Analysis of quotations   As quotations are received they should be recorded on the lower part of the relevant enquiry sheet. Once the full complement of quotations relating to a particular material or sub-contract enquiry are received then they should be checked and then analysed. The checking involves both arithmetic checks and ensuring that all conditions of the enquiry have been complied with.

The estimator is responsible for ensuring that all material prices submitted by suppliers are suitable irrespective of whether the buyer or others have sent out the enquiries. Prices that appear to be incorrect must be ratified with the particular supplier. Prices that have been omitted from all quotes must be obtained from other sources and those missing from individual quotes may need to be obtained later, especially in the case of significant cost items.

Sub-contract quotes that exclude parts of the work and/or with differing allowances for firm price must be adjusted to a common basis to enable a valid comparison of prices to be carried out. For example, one particular quote, **A**, may be firm for only six months whilst the remainder are firm for fourteen months as requested. The builder's estimator must assess the likely price increase of **A**'s work for the remaining eight months and add the cost to **A**'s quote.

The situation is a little more complex when one sub-contractor, **B**, is only prepared to quote for part of the work detailed and the price is the lowest for that equivalent part. The obvious solution is to use **B**'s price and select from the other quotes the lowest price for the remaining work. However, the problem is that bids are based on the whole work. Thus, the sub-contractor selected to carry out the remaining work is likely to withdraw the offer on the grounds that the amount of work has been drastically reduced and the rates are therefore no longer applicable.

Where the same item appears more than once in a quote then the unit rate must be checked in each case to ensure that they do not differ. If different rates are inserted then the particular sub-contractor should be asked to justify the differences or state which one of the rates applies. Thus, pricing inconsistencies are avoided.

Counter offers and qualifications to quotes must be noted and given further consideration once the common basis of each is established. These and any other irregularities together with action taken should be entered on the enquiry sheet, possibly on the flip side for convenience. Thus, all aspects of individual quotes are taken into consideration. Such considerations may therefore result in the estimator not selecting the lowest quote.

General and special attendances   These attendances are generally the same as those outlined for nominated sub-contractors although not shown as separate BQ items. It is accepted practice that the builder provides lighting, water, power, etc, and permits the use of standing scaffold, temporary roads and the like. If domestic sub-contractors require the builder to provide any service, beyond that which is accepted as general attendance, then such requirements must accompany the quote. Such requirements may be contained in a sub-contractor's standard conditions of engagement printed on the rear of the quote.

As the estimator must take account of the cost implications of special requirements, when comparing estimates and formulating the net cost estimate, each must be priced. For example, a roof tiler or floor screeder may specify in the quote that the builder must provide the sand and cement for the work. The estimator must therefore ascertain the quantities of the materials required and the cost thereof. It is assumed that the materials will be mixed by the sub-contractor in his own mixer. However, as such assumptions should not conflict with any local practice which may exist it may be necessary to ask the sub-contractor concerned to qualify the requirement.

The cost of special attendance items on domestic sub-contractors may be incorporated in the unit rates for the work and entered into the measured work section of the BQ or entered into the preliminary section at an appropriate place. The cost of providing sub-contractors with special plant such as mobile scaffold towers, cranes and hard standings for cranes may be allocated similarly although allocation in the preliminaries section is usually preferred.

Quotations late or not received   When quotes are received after the net cost estimate has been completed they should be compared with the quotes used to compile the estimate. If any late quotes are more competitive then any cost savings on the estimate must be calculated and brought to the attention of management at adjudication via the estimator's report.

In situations where quotes are not received the estimator must assess the necessary cost allowances for inclusion in the estimate. This may be achieved by referring to similar data contained in previous tenders or contacting other organisations. If the data is still unavailable from this source then reference to a price book may be made. As prices in such books do not represent actual market prices they must be adjusted by the percentage divergence from market prices which exists for other items. The estimator's report should identify items for which prices cannot be obtained together with the cost solution incorporated into the estimate.

Questions

1   Present reasoned arguments to convince a construction director that it is in the company's interest to make estimating data available to site managers.

2   Describe the ways in which bills of quantities may be used by the planning engineer (planner) and the buyer. Discuss the limitations of the bill of quantities in these respects
    For planning engineer see chapter 2 and chapter 7.

3   Explain the procedures a contractor should follow to ensure that he obtains accurate and reliable quotations from domestic sub-contractors.

7 Pre-contract Planning to Aid Estimating

Purpose of planning Planning is a process which involves the efficient and economical allocation of resources associated with production in advance of the commencement of the work starting. This is basically a plan of action which, when displayed graphically and by other means, conveys to others the intentions of those who have formulated the plan.

The process is normally carried out by a planner or planning department, depending on size of firm, within the builder's organisation. However, this activity often draws from the experience and expertise of other members of the builder's organisation. These include contracts managers, surveyors, estimators, buyers, engineers and plant managers. Their contributions include vital feedback from past and current contracts.

The planning process is one which takes place at various stages of a project:

pre-tender – a realistic plan is developed during the tender period in order to assist in the production of both the cost estimate and the subsequent tender submission. The level of detail attained here is dependant on the time available to analyse the tender documentation. This is assuming that the tender period allowed by the client is sufficiently long enough in relation to the complexity of the project.

In practice detailed pre-tender planning by large and medium sized builders is often reserved for either major projects or those with a high degree of complexity. Other projects may only be planned in outline although often no formal planning whatsoever takes place at this stage. Where a programme has to be submitted with the tender some form of planning is required. The reasons why fully developed detailed pre-tender planning is not feasible are that:

- vast amounts of time are required to programme manually. Thus, the time and cost devoted to such activity at tender would far outweigh that put into the post contract planning activity. Some computerised planning packages will allow complete planning. However, very few builders have sufficient experience and knowledge in the use of such computerised systems as to take advantage of all the facilities offered
- the abortive element (jobs not won) prohibits this continuous deployment of resources

–   many builders do not have the expertise to carry out fully developed detailed planning, at any stage. This is not to say that plans are not developed in detail but that they may well be inaccurately produced.

The decision as to whether detailed planning should take place may be influenced by the relative importance of winning the contract. However, the amount of pre-tender planning that takes place is likely to be limited by the current workload of the planners. Whatever the attitudes of different organisations towards detailed pre-tender planning it is logical that the most crucial time for making detailed plans is prior to submitting a tender. This is so because it is at the tender stage that the builder commits himself to time and cost – after all, these aspects are not considered again until after the contract has been signed. Further, planning is a major factor in winning or losing a tender because the main difference between builders is not in the unit rate calculations but is in the time and method adopted.

Pre-contract planning – once the contract has been signed where planning has previously been carried out the plan is developed in more detail. This will also involve checks to ensure that changes in contract documentation that have occurred since tender are taken into account. Further, the planning approach adopted is also checked for accuracy as it must be adequate for use on site. Where tender planning has not taken place it is necessary to complete a fully developed detailed plan prior to commencement of the works on site.

Contract planning – During the building period, in the event that production is behind programme, short term programmes may have to be prepared on a weekly or monthly basis as necessary. These programmes are not always used to pull back lost time but also to provide details for managing and controlling the site during specific envelopes of time. For instance, a weekly output programme may identify the anticipated labour and plant requirements. This will enable the site staff to acquire and manage the necessary resources in order to maintain production. Further, the achieved productive and financial performance can be monitored and evaluated. Bonus targets and payments may also be controlled on a weekly basis.

In some instances, which may arise at any time during the contract, due to either variations in the work or unforseen circumstances the planning may have to be completely revised. This again places a burden on the planning department which may in turn restrict the time that can be devoted to pre-tender planning activities. The problem may be eased by use of a computerised planning system although such additional work may still be disruptive if the system is over committed.

In instances where projects are running at a loss, irrespective of whether or not the accrued losses can be fully recovered, it is often worthwhile reprogramming the job in order to reduce the deficit. This may involve committing the contractor to more finances. However, such decisions are very crucial to the final cost outcome of a project and must therefore be made after accurate predictions of different solutions have been investigated. A synopsis of the events which took place on a major project illustrates this point:

> here, a contractor under estimated the resources required to erect the frame of a building, the frame being the critical part of the project programme
>
> the contract was destined to be completed late by six weeks
>
> the latest financial appraisal of the work completed showed a loss which when projected would be very substantial
>
> liquidated damages for the project were set at £30th per week.

The project was subsequently reprogrammed, by more experienced planners, to complete on the contract completion date. This exercise together with resource levelling revealed that a specific amount of a particular item of equipment had to be purchased at a price of £70th. The builder hesitated in committing more cash to the loss making situation until he was convinced that the revised planning would work.

By acting on the new information the builder was actually able to save eight weeks on the programme, as opposed to six, thus not only managing to avoid damages and site costs but also offsetting most of the additional outlay through savings of two weeks' site overheads.

Planning objectives   The objective of planning is to provide site management with an efficient production strategy which will meet the requirements of specific contracts. Here, the two main considerations are those of time and cost. These elements whilst being equally important, as they are interdependent, will affect the project differently. Therefore, the proportions of each need to be considered in order to achieve the optimum plan. Consequently, alternative solutions for the proportions of time and cost should be considered to determine the most effective combination for the job under consideration.

At the tender stage further objectives must be realised. In addition to production requirements there are those of both estimating and management to be met. These objectives relate to the overall aim of winning the contract at an acceptable price. The estimator requires such information concerning production planning that will assist in the preparation of a realistic net cost estimate. Management also needs to be provided with details of production planning when deciding on a tender sum. The more a plan is developed then the more certain it becomes.

Thus, a high level of certainty is important to help foster better management decisions. Here, the management must be confident that the plan of action is such that it is:

- accurate
- the most suitable solution
- possible to achieve
- confined exclusively to the basic obligations imposed by the tender documentation.

This should facilitate the preparation of a net cost estimate which will represent a true financial representation of the builder's intentions for subsequent validation by management.

Tasks to be performed

The process of planning commences with establishing in detail the manner in which the work is to be executed. This is followed by arranging activities of work into a logical sequence together with the assessment of their respective durations. The durations of the activities collectively provide the total time scale for the project.

The following is the sequence of tasks that need to be performed in order to produce an effective plan:

- *visits to site and consultants* – opportunity to ratify any matters that are not covered by the documentation provided by the client. Ideally this is the first task but is often left until later in the process for incorporation into the plan
- *method statement(s)* – written record of the proposed plan for use as a working document
- *site layout* – record of the allocation of site functions and facilities together with their respective location, annotated on the site layout drawing
- *programme of work* – visual presentation of activities and associated durations in diagrammatic format for ease of reading:
  - *logic diagram* – complex but comprehensive logical sequence of activities as a basis for and to underpin the more simplistic but effective method of data presentation offered by a bar (Gantt) chart. Often due to the lack of time or expertise in the area this part of the planning process is ignored.
  - *bar chart* – provides a readily understood visual statement

of individual and overall activity sequencing and timing. A few builders consider this to be superfluous and prefer to rely entirely on a logic diagram. However, in such cases a bar chart is produced for the benefit of those professionals that are not as well conversed with logic diagrams
- resource scheduling and levelling – establishing resource requirements – the balance to give consistent levels throughout the job, often shown in graphical format.

Visits During the tender period it is important to establish any other matters which need to be taken into account beyond the official data provided. With alteration work, especially when only a plan and specification is provided, it is essential to visit the site in order to determine the true extent of the work. For example, one aspect of the work may require the mortar joints of the brickwork to be raked out and repointed. An inspection of the brickwork could reveal that the mortar may have deteriorated or be of a weak mix such that it can be removed with little effort. Alternatively, the reverse may be true.

New build sites also have physical characteristics which need to be considered. These include location, width and height and other restrictions for site access, fencing requirements, location of existing manholes for disposal of surplus water and temporary connections for toilets, location and condition of existing structures including trees and any obstructions, degree of natural site drainage, water courses, type of soil and water table may be visible here or on an adjacent site, location of existing services and the like.

These and other points, which help with both planning and estimating, cannot be fully answered by scrutinising the tender documents. Apart from this, a true perspective of the site and surrounding areas can only be attained by inspection. For instance, what may seem from the drawings to be a straight forward site location could turn out to be quite the opposite in that it may be situated on a very congested one way system.

Visiting the architect is also recommended because whilst looking through the drawings and discussing various details it will enable the builder to establish a number of important points regarding the project:

- establish better understanding of both the client requirements and the architects intentions
- view any drawings which have been finalised but not issued as part of the tender documentation
- extent to which the design is complete
- understanding shown by the architect regarding the practical implications of the design

- specific problems identified by the architect including any solutions offered
- architect's solutions to problems identified by the builder
- restrictions to the builder's proposed sequence and method of working – this may include discussions to overcome any problem
- possible changes in specification or design to help improve buildability.

These points are not only helpful at tender but also at the pre-contract stage, especially the last point.

Such visits may not be confined to the architect's office as other consultants such as the quantity surveyor and the various consultant engineers may provide further information. For example, the services engineer can discuss critical aspects of the job concerning the integration of major services requirements into the builder's general programme of work. Further, physical problems of production associated with the services installations must also be considered.

Having spoken to the various consultants the builder is able to assess the type of working relationships that are likely to prevail during the project. This aspect needs to be considered as personalities are very important when dealing with people on a daily basis. A good working relationship is desirable as it leads to all parties working together as a team. Thus, problems can be resolved amicably without compromising individual interests and responsibilities.

Any queries which arise from the visits must be resolved by the consultant responsible for making such decisions. This may be possible during a visit but is often dealt with at a later date together with any other queries that have been recorded.

Method statements   A method statement is intended to describe in detail the sequence and manner in which the main parts of the work are to be carried out. It is produced from the documentation provided by the client together with other information collected/produced to help prepare both the cost estimate and production plan. Thus, management, estimating and production personnel need to use the definitive statement of the method. The statement may be for all to use or alternatively three individual statements may be produced which emphasise the individual needs of each user. For example, management may require less detailed and more general than that required by others whereas the estimator is more concerned with specific aspects such as resource and duration details.

Many builders do not consider method statements to be of use.

Such an attitude is not surprising considering that the method statements produced are usually inappropriate. This together with the fact that many personnel have never been provided with an adequate method statement perpetuates the apathy towards their production.

A common approach to the presentation of method statements is simply to list independently as many activities as possible together with the corresponding labour and plant requirements. However, a more appropriate approach is to describe the activities and resource requirements in a manner which relates to their sequencing/timing. Note that the extent to which the sequencing can be predicted at the early stages of tendering is limited. Therefore, a more definitive statement of sequence must be developed in order to produce the final plan. The merits of a sequenced approach are evident from the part method statement, table 7.1, produced from the site details shown in figure 7.1.

The drawings in figure 7.1 relate to the construction of two identical buildings, opposite handed, on one site. Other work includes a new retaining wall, positioned in front of the unstable

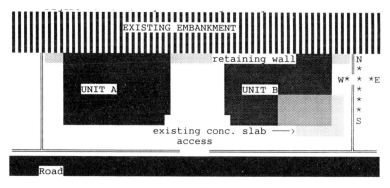

PLAN

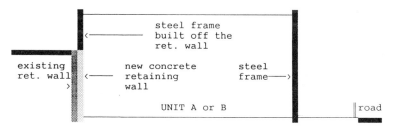

Sectional Elevation

Figure 7.1   Site layout drawings for job reference 1

existing wall, together with the removal of an area of existing concrete floor slab, located to the South East of the site.

The intention is first to commence unit A and follow up with unit B so that the phasing of the two units allows continuity of work. In order to proceed with the erection of each unit the integral sections of the retaining wall must be complete. Thus, commencement and subsequent completion of specific parts of the retaining wall must be achieved as soon as possible.

The suggested sequence of early production activities is as follows:

— commence site clearance and reduce level dig, starting from the NW of the site and working both out and across to the SE
— as soon as the NW area is clear the work to the retaining wall is to be commenced. The construction of the wall will continue until complete
— concrete slab to be broken up as the excavation proceeds.

Activity	Labour and plant	Resource (number)	Output (per hour)	Duration (weeks)	Hours req'd
Excavation reduced level					
dig	Banksman	1		<u>2000</u>	68
2000m3	Drott B100	1	18m3	30x38*	68
	JCB 811	1	12m3		68
	8m3 lorries	5		=1.75	340
				====	
foundations	Banksman	2		<u>300</u>	88
300m3	JCB 811	1	7m3	7x38	44
	8m3 lorries	2			88
				=1.13	
				====	
break up					
concrete	JCB 811 with			<u>120</u>	
120m3	heavy duty			6x38	
	breaker				
	attachment**	1	6m3		21
	Drott B100	1		=0.53	21
	8m3 lorries	2		====	42

* Here, one hour is deducted from the 39 hour week for overlap of machines working, refuelling, oiling, greasing and cleaning down. A 39 hour week is, however, used when calculating the hours required
** Note that either a two tool compressor or arrow breaker may be used in lieu of the JCB with hammer.

Table 7.1   Method statement, early section relating to ground works: common approach

Irrespective of the level of detail included in this example it is clear that there is no indication as to when activities are carried out. Further, if the statement was to follow this approach then the next activity, namely the retaining wall, would be presented in the same isolated manner. Thus, the method statement needs to be extended to include some indication as to the sequence of operations and assumptions upon which the method is based.

This may be achieved by either inserting an additional column within the statement[1] or alternatively writing the statement in the form of a report. The latter method is considered the more appropriate as firstly it facilitates the consideration of many related and interactive activities/issues that need to be dealt with and secondly there are no columns to inhibit the depth of detail that may have to be included within the statement. Both points are important if the method statement is to be of any use beyond that of a glorified pricing schedule for estimators.

One important aspect of producing a method statement, not mentioned so far, includes the review and evaluation of alternative methods and sequences. This is an important element of method development and is usually carried out in conjunction with the site layout details – which may also be the subject of review in order to either increase the usage of the site or facilitate alternative methods. Here, labour, plant and equipment for the main activities are considered, including alternatives and combinations. These will not only be evaluated for time and cost but also for their affect on other operations generally. The objective is to investigate the cost and time implications of different methods and sequences to establish the most efficient solution.

A method statement should also include details relating to access, hoisting, distribution, accommodation, storage, shoring and other supports, special protection, temporary works and the like. Many of these issues coincide with and are therefore considered when the site layout is being developed.

The Code of estimating practice provides a useful basis from which to prepare a method statement, and further highlights the importance of the document. Because of the detailed nature of the method statement, many builders find the document a useful vehicle for qualifying their tenders.

Site layout

The site layout relates to issues concerning the site in terms of both its use and location of plant, equipment and services. Facilities and their location are determined by a number of factors:

- constraints imposed by both the size and nature of the site together with the building work to be accommodated thereon
- the information contained in the method statements. This includes the likely number of operatives and staff to be on site at any one point in time, the type of plant to be used and the construction methods to be adopted

- the site overheads/preliminaries requirements
- the requirements of the Working Rule Agreement (WRA) issued by the National Joint Council for the building industry.

Although many of the considerations are common to various situations as each site is unique, the appropriate solution is likely to vary considerably. For example, a confined site (in relation to the building work), figure 7.2, will generally pose more problems than a large site. However, due to the limited amount of land or sites available for development it is usually out of economic necessity that the full use of such land is achieved irrespective of the nature of the site. Thus, problems are likely to be encountered on a high proportion of projects.

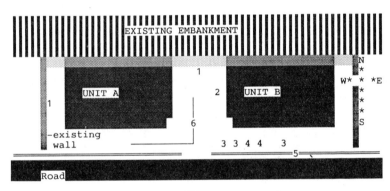

PLAN

Legend:	1	Open storage	4	Toilets
	2	Closed storage	5	Perimeter fencing
	3	Site cabins	6	Turning area

Figure 7.2   Site layout drawings for job reference 1

Job reference 1, figure 7.2, is a typical confined site which presents many problems in respect to site layout. Numbers one to six on the drawing indicate the location for each of the site provisions included on the legend. Whilst these provisions are not intended to represent every conceivable aspect of site layout they will provide an appreciation of the issues involved:

Open storage

Two areas have been designated. The West area is to be used early in the contract for stacking and sorting of the bar reinforcement for the retaining wall and stanchion bases. The North area is to be used throughout the contract for storing bricks, blocks, paving slabs, drainage goods and the like. This location is easily accessible for deliveries and subsequent distribution around the site. Other areas may have to be used on similar sites where large quantities of on site materials cannot be avoided.

Closed storage

This is positioned not only for ease of access but for security as it is also positioned in full view of the site office. The store will be a small lockable sectional type, size 1.80 m × 1.20 m – the size of cabin being determined by its usage which in this case will be limited to small consumables such as dpcs, dpms, wall ties, insulation boards, drain pipe couplings and the like.

Materials such as doors, frames, linings, architraves, skirtings and ironmongery are of minimal quantities. Therefore, iron-mongery will be locked in the site office along with any small power tools and surveying equipment whereas the timber will be stored in one of the units on hardboard sheets to protect the floor surface.

If sub-contractors wish to bring onto site their own storage facilities there will be limited space available adjacent but North of the builder's store plus space on the south boundary to the West of the site access.

Site cabins

Three cabins have been provided. These are located to the East of the site access together with the toilets due to the fact that the mains water, electricity and drainage all enter the site in this area. Thus, distribution of these services is kept to a minimum.

The cabin immediately adjacent the site access is the builder's site office and is therefore strategically placed to oversee both the site and the point of access. This will be a small portable cabin with jack leg mountings and crane lifting hooks, size 4.80 m × 2.60 m (interntal floor dimensions) suitable to house the site foreman, both the visiting surveyor and contracts manager and accommodate periodic site meetings. The cabin is to be hoisted into position by the hire company using a telescopic crane, as will all other portables.

Note that cabins over 2.70 m wide may have to be transported to site under police escort. If space on site is too limited the site office may be stacked on top of the mess room which is currently located next to the site office. The cabin will have two filing cabinets, one chest for drawings, one double desk, one large table, six chairs, one telephone, two double socket outlets, one fluorescent light, one heater, one small wash hand basin with hot and cold water and a first aid cabinet as required by the WRA.

The mess cabin is situated adjacent the site office, this being the same type and size as the office. Hot water and drying facilities as required by the WRA will be included in addition to tables, benches, chairs, one lockable cabin, socket outlets and one fluorescent light.

The cabin located to the East of the toilets is the office for the clerk of works. This cabin is situated well away from the site office to give privacy to the builder's staff when discussing sensitive matters. The contract documents specify a cabin size 2.80 m × 2.60 m with heating, lighting, power and telephone. The office will contain one single desk and chair together with a filing cabinet. If the cabin size is not specified in the documents then the smallest cabin possible is allocated. Also, if a telephone is not specified then one is not provided. Note that if the client requires facilities beyond those specified then they can be provided at an additional cost.

Toilets

The toilet facilities are located between the mess and the clerk of works office, sited over an existing manhole to reduce drainage costs. This is a two compartment portable mains unit, each fitted with a wc and wash basin with drinking water facilities, overall size 2.53 m × 1.33 m. One compartment is male and the other is female. The number of toilets required on any site is specified, as a legal requirement, in the WRA. An analysis of weekly labour requirements for this project ensures that the requirement for sanitary conveniences is complied with.

Although not always observed by many builder's the provision of female facilities is part of the sanitary requirements. With the growing number of females within the industry at all levels those builder's that do not provide separate female facilities run the risk of being taken to court for sex discrimination.

In addition to mains flushing portable units there are also mobile and no-mains units available if so required. Chemical toilets are sometimes used although, as these are very primitive, workers and staff now expect better facilities on site.

Perimeter fencing

The front of the site is to be cordoned off from the road and footpath by means of a 3 m high plywood hoarding secured to timber supports, erected behind the existing boundary dwarf wall. A lockable double gate will be provided at the site access point. The reminder of the site is enclosed by existing high walls. The project sign board is to be located above the hoarding adjacent the site entrance, this being a prominent position.

Turning area

Whilst short vehicles may adequately turn in this area it is anticipated that the majority of long vehicles delivering goods will reverse onto the site.

Mortar mixing area

No provision is to be made for mixing mortar on site and therefore pre-mixed tubs of mortar will be used. This decision is taken because of the absence of a suitable area for mixing in terms of space, materials storage and disposal of the large quantities of water required for cleaning out the drum after each mix. Note that when mixing areas are allocated they are normally located as near to the water supply as practically possible.

Logic diagram   This process is commonly referred to as network analysis. It is necessary to produce a logic diagram in order to determine both the order and duration of activities. This also identifies those activities which are critical, ie affected by late start or finish dates, together with the extent of float for each non critical activity, ie the extent to which such activities may be delayed without disrupting/delaying other events.

Float can be separated into a number of components, namely total float, free float and interfering float.[2] Early start/finish and late start/finish time can be derived using the different calculations. However, such calculations are virtually impossible to carry out in practice. Also, the data produced makes the planning process more complex than it is already. Therefore, in this text float is the difference between the time available and the time allowed for each activity (earliest finish/latest finish).

The concept of critical and non critical activity is outlined in the following example of activities extracted from a random programme:

1   excavate foundation bases and slab – four days (duration)

2   hardcore and blinding – four days, provision for services cannot commence until 1 above is complete

3   provision for services – one day, cannot commence before 2 above is complete

4   reinforcement to foundations – four days, cannot start until 2 above is complete

5   formwork to foundations – three days, cannot start until 2 above is complete

6   concrete to foundations – five days, cannot start until 3, 4 and 5 above are complete.

For the purpose of this example these activities are best expressed in bar format, as figure 7.3. From the chart, activities 1, 2, 4 and 6 are critical (these representing the critical path of the grouped activity) in that if activity 1 is delayed then the following three are affected, if activity 2 is delayed then the following two are affected, and so on. However, activities 3 and 5 are not critical due to the fact that they have float, indicated by the dotted bar extension.

This simply means that the time allowed for these activities is less than the respective time envelope within which each has to be carried out. Thus, the activities may be started at any time as long as they are completed by the times specified.

Activity 3, having the greater float, can start (and finish) at any time during the four day period. Therefore, there is margin for this activity to take longer than 1 day, the extent of which depends on how early it is started.

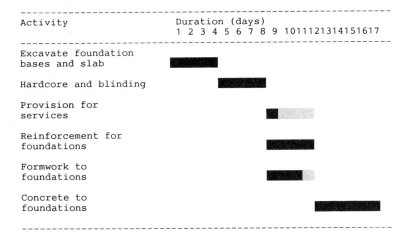

Figure 7.3   Bar chart showing durations of activities

Activity 5 has only a float of one day, therefore it must start on day ten (day two of the activity period) at the latest in order to be completed before day 13.

For any project the logic is established by first separating the job into parts, analysing these separate parts and then linking the parts to form the complete sequence. The process involves breaking down each part of the work (sub-network) into the activities to be carried out, charting these activities, calculating activity durations and then linking the activities, related to each sub-network, together whilst observing the start and finish date relationships.

When the various sub-networks are complete then they are linked together to form the final network. Sub-networks are necessary as it is not usually practical to produce a network by simply starting at the beginning and working through to the end due to the complexity of production organisational and activity interrelationships.

The two main techniques used in network analysis are *critical path analysis* (CPA) and *precedence diagram*. These are very similar in appearance due to the fact that each comprise of a series of squares (circles are common with CPA diagrams) joined by lines in the form of arrows. The squares are referred to as nodes. However, with CPA the arrow represents the activity to be represented whilst with precedence the activity is represented by the node.

Critical path analysis

This approach is not recommended for planning building work because it does not work, as demonstrated by the following example:

> Two sub-networks have been produced and now need linking together, figure 7.4. Here, activity D has to be completed before L can start but does not have to be complete before activities M and N. Activity D is therefore critical. Because the nodes, which do not represent activities, are linked together using this approach then the arrow link is made between nodes 68 and 96. This is an incorrect representation of the sequencing because by linking D to 68 which in turn is linked to 96 the network is showing that activities L, M and N cannot start until D is

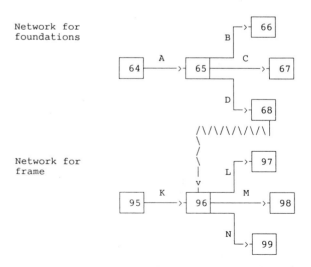

Figure 7.4   Linking two CPA sub-networks

complete. A network can also be affected in this manner during the contract when facilitating architects instructions (variations and extras), resulting in major complex changes to the network.

Precedence diagram – single and double node

This approach is recommended as it does not have the problems that are inherent with CPA. The technique used to produce the network may be either single or double node. Double node is more sophisticated and therefore more versatile. However, as this is a relatively new technique it is rarely used.

The way in which the single node technique overcomes the fundamental problem which occurs with CPA is demonstrated in figure 7.5. Here, activities M and N are not reliant on completion of D. This therefore accommodates the constraints relating to the two sub-networks features in figure 7.4. Note that the abbreviation FS may also be added to denote that the arrow link is finish to start. This means that as soon as D is finished L will start. The abbreviation SS (start to start) together with the lag time may be used in other instances.

Thus, in bar format FS and SS 5 annotations become:

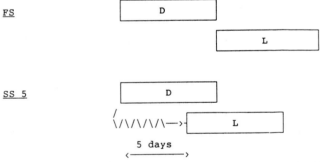

With this technique the node represents the whole activity from start to finish. Having completed the network and determined durations the early start/finish (ES, EF) and late start/finish (LS, LF) calculations can be carried out. Thus, ES, EF, LS, LF times can be entered for each activity:

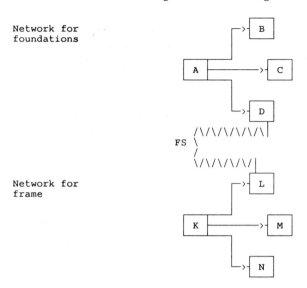

Figure 7.5   Linking two single node precedence sub-networks

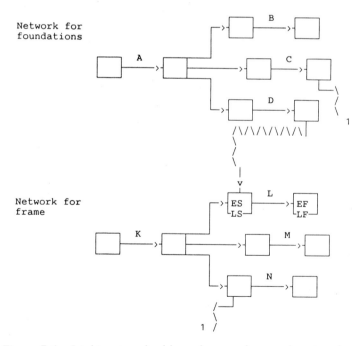

Figure 7.6   Linking two double node precedence sub-networks

Double node works on the same principle as single node but utilises two nodes to separately identify the start of an activity and the end of that activity. Using the example network shown for single node, figure 7.5, the double node technique is represented in figure 7.6. In this example an extra link has been introduced, connecting the finish of activity C with the start of activity N. This demonstrates that link arrows do not have to be continuous. The use of a broken link arrow (dummy) is an important feature when developing a complex network as it avoids endless arrows intersecting – these being likely to merge and therefore difficult to follow.

Network development

Whether the single or double node technique is used a precedence diagram is best developed using a grid system, figure 7.7. This allows the start and finish points of a broken link arrow to be clearly identified. Thus, activities located at any point on the grid are easily linked together.

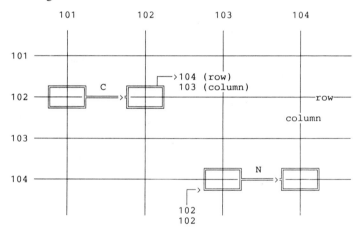

Figure 7.7   Precedence development on a grid system

Note that during the network development when start/finish times and durations are being considered all known and anticipated lost working days or weeks need to be taken into account and included in the calculations. This includes days lost due to holiday periods and seasonal adverse weather.

Bar chart   The builder's main production programme is in the form of a bar (Gantt) chart which displays all the main activities and their duration, figure 7.8. Whilst activities are listed in sequence the bar format precludes the level of detailed interrelationships afforded with the network. Thus, the sequencing achieved is only an outline. To some extent this limitation is overcome with simplistic charts by linking bars, that are dependant on preceding activities, with arrows. This presentation is known as a *linked bar chart*.

Bar charts are produced directly from the network data, durations being calculated for all work on a similar basis as that shown in table 7.1. However, the calculations are carried out in relation to

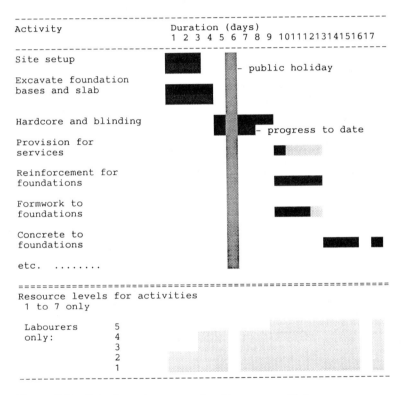

Figure 7.8   Bar chart: incorporating histogram of labourer requirements

the main items of work. Sundry items are accounted for within these calculations rather than by additional calculations. Sub-contract work is dealt with in the same manner using feedback from other projects.

Alternatively, a better indication of duration and phased visits may be attained through discussions with sub-contractors. Note that all time and resource calculations must be realistic to avoid over run of the contract period.

Delivery dates for key materials such as steel may be indicated on the programme. In addition, key stages of the work, such as when the building is water tight, may be shown.

The programme together with the method statement and site layout details are useful to the estimator when calculating preliminaries, especially for items such as plant and accommodation which have major time related cost components. The information on the programme can also be used to produce cash flow forecasts and provide a basis for operational estimating if available at the time of pricing the work.

Resource scheduling and levelling   The resource requirements are established from the programme, as indicated in figure 7.8, by working across the sheet in columns and abstracting out of the planning data those resources that the builder wishes to display. This may be in terms of overall labour, plant and supervision or alternatively broken down into specific trades (bricklayers, joiners, labourers), plant items and staffing, for each week of the programme.

Having done this, where requirements fluctuate they need to be smoothed out as much as possible to achieve a more constant level:

Bricklayers: original   revised

Because the revised schedule has a direct affect on activities the programme must be revised to accommodate this. As other resources are balanced they too will affect the programme. The reprogramming then becomes a very complicated and time consuming operation. This operation is thus not feasible as a manual process during the tender stage and is unlikely to be attempted at a later date for the same reason. Some computerised planning packages do incorporate an automatic revised programme facility which responds to inputs of alternative resource levels. Such packages therefore make resource balancing a reality and as a result the resources correctly determine durations as opposed to the durations dictating resource levels.

At tender stage, rather than attempting to balance all the resources the common practice is to identify one major aspect of the job, resource balance and then fit the remainder of the job around it. Quite often the resource levels within a programme are either too high or too low in relation to the actual levels that are practically manageable. In such instances the levels also need to be revised.

This may have a number of implications on the programme.

Take for example a situation where a programme has been completed to meet the completion date. Analysis of the resources shows a requirement of 50 bricklayers for the brickwork section. At this stage brickwork is identified as being the major single aspect of the job. The contracts manager may, using his experience, decide that it is only practical to employ 30 bricklayers due to the difficulty in managing and/or acquiring a greater number.

The revised programme is subsequently produced, incorporating the new resource level. Unfortunately the new completion date occurs beyond that required. This means that the programme must now be revised again. The revised brickwork details are next fed into the network and the sequencing of other activities is centred around brickwork to achieve the required completion date. The result of this procedure is the production of the final programme, which displays achievable production targets.

Production control   The planning data may be used to determine the criticality of a project which in turn may be used to provide site staff with a check on production progress. This is achieved by allocating points of criticality to each activity on the programme. Two sets of calculations are derived, the first using the earliest start dates and the second using the latest start dates.

By allocating the points back to the respective programmed activities the total number of points to be completed each month can be established. A cumulative curve of these monthly totals is then plotted for each set of calculations. The two curves run side by side sharing the same start and finish points, thus taking a form similar to that of a pea pod. During the contract the actual points achieved are plotted against these curves to check production levels. Production is on target if the actual line plotted remains between the two curves. Problems occur when the plotted line moves to the right – outside the area between the two curves.

Points for each activity are calculated using the equation:

Criticality of activity $= \dfrac{D}{T} \times 100$; where D and T are represented by:

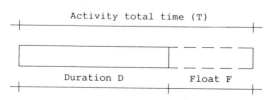

Note that the greater the number of points allocated then the more critical the work is.

Integration of estimating and planning   Where integration exists between the two functions the extent to which this takes place is either total or partial. Total integration is not common with builders as it involves the two factions jointly developing all the tasks within the planning process.

The favoured approach is for both the planner and the estimator to initially agree an outline plan of methods and resources, each then proceeds separately with their respective tasks and on completion meet again to compare time and cost solutions. Occasionally progress update meetings may be held at intermediate stages of development or, as is usual, on an ad hoc basis.

If upon completion of the two processes there exists significant discrepancies then the differences must be reviewed to determine which solution is to be presented to management for consideration at adjudication. Issues likely to be the subject of review include labour and plant allocations, durations of major activities and their affect on the overall project duration. This process is referred to as reconciliation. Usually the matter can be and is required to be resolved before the adjudication meeting. In very exceptional circumstances it may not be possible to arrive at a solution, thus, the alternatives may have to be put before management for further consideration.

References

1 COOKE, B, *Contract planning and contract procedures*, second edition reprinted, Macmillan 1987, pp 30.
2 HARRIS, F, and McCAFFER, R, *Modern construction management*, second edition reprinted, Collins 1985, pp 16–17.

Questions

1 Discuss ways in which the contractor's planning engineer can make a vital contribution to the estimating process.

2 Describe the use of pre-tender programmes by estimators in the evaluation of:
(a) plant
(b) site supervision
(c) site accommodation.

3 Explain the function of the following documents in the preparation of a tender:
(a) Method statements
(b) The site layout drawing.

4 Evaluate the role of project programme in the determination of an estimate.

8 Project Overheads

Scope of preliminaries   The main part of the preliminaries section that must be priced concerns the builder's general cost items and client's requirements. These are necessary to support the site and collectively are referred to as either site or project or indirect overheads. The cost implications of project overheads along with the obligations imposed by the contract conditions relating to any project must be included in the net cost estimate. Here, all matters which influence costs must be considered. Items covered include police and safety regulations, restricted working, advertising, noise, nuisance, protection, programmes and progress meetings, recording data for consultants, temporary services, supervision, hutting, plant, cleaning, hoardings, name board, surveying equipment and the like, special facilities such as office and telephone for the use of the client, cleaning, drying out, insurance arrangements, firm or fluctuating price and bond requirement where applicable.

Further, the contract conditions will, unless required to be established by the builder, contain the proposed contract commencement and completion dates or duration. This data may have a cost implication where a very short construction period is required. Otherwise the information is used to aid the estimating/tendering process including the pricing of time related cost items, assessing firm price adjustment, preparing a construction programme and subsequent cash flow forecast.

These preliminary items tend to be required generally on most projects with minor additions and variations to suit specific situations. However, as each project is unique the implications and requirements imposed by such individual clauses are different in every case. Thus, the preliminaries should be priced on the merits of each project. Another factor that must not be overlooked is the importance of preliminaries as a competitive element within the tender sum. Careful consideration must therefore be given to this area of cost.

Types of site overheads   A synopsis of the types of site overheads, classified by function, may be summarised as follows:

> *site set-up* – Surveying equipment, hutting including rates and any associated site preparation, hoardings, name board, related transport and hoisting facilities

services – Providing programmes, providing samples and testing of materials, insurances if specified as the builder's responsibility, telephone(s), water, lighting and power

supervision and transport – Management/staff, provision of transport for site staff plus general transport for the collection of sundry materials and ferrying operatives to and from the site where necessary

plant – Electrical and mechanical plant (dumpers, mortar mixers, cranes, hoists, pumps and the like) and none mechanical plant such as scaffold

site maintenance – Protecting tthe works,* temporary roads, maintenance of public roads, drying out, cleaning and making good defects

contractual impositions – Working restrictions, fluctuations/firm price assessment, liquidated damages due to possible job overrun and any other quantifiable risks that are identified.

For pricing purposes each item can be broken down into smaller elements and then segregated into fixed and time related components. This eliminates the chance of price duplication and further, enables each cost component to be identified and priced in a manner which reflects the way in which such costs are incurred.

The SMM7 makes a distinction between site overheads by way of those which relate to the employer's requirements and those which relate to the contractor's general cost items. The code of estimating practice also makes this distinction. Whether or not the builder wishes to maintain the distinction when allocating costs within the preliminaries section of the net cost estimate similar items may be dealt with together for convenience. Thus for example, the assessment of costs for the client's hutting can be considered at the same time as the builder's hutting requirements even if to be shown separately. Another area where joint assessment is appropriate concerns the provision of a separate telephone for the sole use of the client.

The items to be considered for pricing purposes are general cost centres, some of which contain a number of specific cost centres.

---

* Whilst protection items are included in the measured work section they relate to specific aspects of the work. Here, the protection item relates to theft and vandalism, especially broken windows.

Note also that the provision of both insurance and water are included at the back of a BQ at the end of the general summary. The reason for this is that the cost of such items are based on the contract value. This is not quite the case with water as only the water corporation's charge is based on contract value. The cost of the stand pipes, distribution pipes and associated ground works depends on the builder's specific requirements.

Specific cost centres, or elements, are allocated to a particular general cost centre on the basis of group similarity. The code of estimating practice sets out in detail a schedule of preliminary items in the form of readily identifiable cost centres which are free from repetition or overlap. Each cost centre is conveniently broken down into appropriate elements and incorporates separate fixed and time related cost components. In addition, the schedule allows insertion of the individual labour, material, plant and sub-contractor costs within each element total cost.

A list of preliminary items must be prepared prior to the commencement of pricing. This involves identifying the relevant cost centres for the project in question. The list of cost centres, and components thereof, constitutes a schedule of site overheads that are proposed to be included in the estimate. When drafting the schedule it is prudent to allow spaces for miscellaneous items to accommodate those such as general site labourers plus any notes and comments that need to be taken into account by future users of the schedule. However, whether the format recommended in the COEP or an appropriate alternative is adopted is not important as long as the general principles are followed and most importantly that the same format is adhered to for every project. This is not to say that formats should not be amended to meet unique situations or reviewed/revised to meet changing trends.

The benefit of adopting a standardised approach is that of efficiency through familiarity, namely greater consistency, enhanced speed of working and the elimination of errors through duplication.

This also facilitates the development of a compatible data bank which can be used to validate each and every part of the process. Note that the principle of adopting a disciplined approach applies to procedures generally and therefore should not be interpreted as being confined to this particular process.

Having prepared the preliminaries schedule in the form of fixed and time related cost centre components then the subsequent pricing stage can begin.

Whilst the preliminaries section of a BQ is presented in such a manner as to provide the opportunity for builders to enter a price against every item only a limited number of items are actually priced. Thus, it is unlikely that any builder would price more than 20 main items. However, some items may in fact contain a number of items. For example site supervision could include contract manager, agent and QS whilst site accommodation could include hutting together with the associated items of transport, hoisting, service connections, repairs and maintenance. In addition, on inspection of a priced preliminaries section the prices contained therein may be misleading as some costs may have been distributed throughout other sections of the estimate. This is important when setting incentive (bonus) and other financial targets from bill prices.

One factor which influences the choice of items to be priced and the estimating approach to be adopted is the relative cost significance of each item. Thus, an allowance for possible job over run, based on the value of liquidated damages, may be considered for inclusion in the net cost estimate whereas the provision of staff should be included. More time is also devoted to the detailed estimating of costs for major cost items whereas the cost of minor items may be approximated.

Research[1] into the pricing practices of selected building contractors on a number of estimates they prepared revealed a number of interesting points concerning preliminaries as follows:

over 90% of the value of preliminaries value is contained in six items

builders normally price 16 main items

most items appear to be priced in detail and those that are not priced in detail rarely exceed £100 in value

over 88% of costs have a time component

The 16 main items priced are shown in table 8.1 together with their relative proportion of total preliminaries costs.

```
-------------------------------------------------------------------
  Preliminary items                % of total prelims value
-------------------------------------------------------------------
   1    Staff                           28.6
   2    Plant                           20.8
   3    Scaffold                        16.8
   4    Hutting (site accommodation)    11.8
   5    Power (including lighting)       7.0
   6    Cleaning                         5.2   ----- 90.2%
   7    Hoardings                        2.0
   8    Security                         1.7
   9    Temporary roads                  1.6
  10    Insurance                        1.6
  11    Telephone                        1.3
  12    Water                            0.5
  13    Protection                       0.4
  14    Drying out                       0.3
  15    Testing                          0.3
  16    Frost precautions                0.1
                                       -----
                                       100.0
                                       =====
-------------------------------------------------------------------
```

Table 8.1   Value of individual preliminary items expressed as a proportion of total preliminary costs, in rank order
Source: Building Technology and Management, *April 1983*

Note that whilst the six most significant cost items accounted for 90% of the preliminaries value on each of the jobs monitored there may be some variation depending on the size and type of work undertaken together with the organisational structure of each firm.

Nature of site overheads   Preliminary items are generally described in such a manner as to allow builders the scope to decide on the extent of the provision within or beyond that outline. Thus, preliminary requirements are often expressed in general terms. This is because there are usually a number of alternative solutions which would satisfy the item. Here, the options relating say to hoardings and site security are chain link fencing, timber boarding, pale chestnut fencing, fabric reinforcement secured to timber posts, night/weekend watchman, security organisation and on certain sites a combination of alternatives or no provision at all. As a consequence the quantity, quality and value of many preliminary items allowed in each competing builder's tender will vary considerably.

Take for example hutting, one builder may decide to allow portable jack-leg cabins for all requirements whilst another may opt to combine such cabins with sectional cabins (erected and dismantled in sections) and maybe a trailor type or ex-railway carriage. In addition, cabins to be provided by each builder are likely to be different in size with the possible exception of the client's cabin if the size is specified in the tender documentation. Further, the provision may be made up of either hired or owned cabins or a mixture of the two.

The provision of hoisting facilities is again likely to vary between builders. Here one builder may elect to use a tower crane throughout the building of the entire work whilst another may limit its use to superstructure and another may opt for a number of barrow hoists strategically positioned for maximum efficiency with an additional provision for bringing to site a mobile telescopic crane for specific hoisting requirements.

Another aspect of pricing preliminaries involves the provision of insurances, water for the works, lighting and power and the like. The cost of insurances, covering injury to persons, buildings and occasionally that of adjoining property (usually the subject of a PC sum) together with that of power to the site is established by obtaining quotations for each particular service. Water is charged by the authorities as a percentage of the contract sum.

In addition to charges for service supplies there are other costs which relate to site distribution and subsequent connections/disconnecting, quarterly charges and power consumed as in the case of electricity. Telephone costs include installation and quarterly standing and consumer charges.

Allowances for all costs must be included in the tender sum, many of which have to be estimated based on records of consumption levels on recent similar projects. Note that where there is no requirement for the builder to provide a separate telephone for the client's use the BQ may contain a provisional sum for telephone calls made on behalf of the client. In such cases the builder is obviously not required to carry out a cost exercise on that particular element at the tender stage.

Whilst the considerations vary between items one underlying factor common to most is the need for quantification. This relies heavily on the experience and judgement of both the estimator and planner. The provision of temporary roads and hard standings requires the application of such expertise. Here, builders will earmark different areas to be hardcored, allow varying depths, possibly using different materials. To avoid the cost of reinstating the external works formation levels, involving excavating and off-site disposal of hardcore fill, some estimators will allow for excavating the soil to a level below formation to facilitate the depth of initial fill. Thus, the contract hardcore, required as sub-base for external pavings, can be spread to the specified depth directly over the initial soiled hardcore.

Costs of specific provisions such as lighting and power generally change on each job because of factors such as the distribution distance from the supply point, seasonal demands, size and duration of the project, periodic price increases and special requirements such as a three-phase power supply. However, the cost of other preliminary items such as hutting, plant, staffing and the like are not only influenced by similar factors to these but also the individual appraisal of each project by a particular builder.

Such appraisals result in the allocation of different provisions to each site. Thus, a builder's preliminaries for any specific project are unique not only to that particular organisation but also to that particular project. For instance, a four storey hotel of complex design located in the city centre will require different preliminary items to those required for a small housing development of similar value. It is therefore unwise to prepare tenders by allocating costs to each preliminary item on a percentage of total cost basis as there is no correlation between preliminaries and contract value.

Solutions to cost and time (where applicable) alternatives are established to determine the most appropriate provision to meet the needs of both the builder and client. Having completed the pricing of all preliminary items the total sum is added to the net cost estimate. This may eventually involve inserting a price against each* preliminary item that has been considered. Allocating these

---

* Some builders spread the preliminaries cost over selected items, usually items that they consider either cannot be interfered with (adjusted) by the architect and quantity surveyor or will result in some later advantage. However, all items may be

continued. . .

prices into a BQ is generally left until after adjudication as management decisions may either alter the preliminaries provisions or fix a tender sum so low that monies have to be deducted from the estimate.

The most convenient place to make the adjustment is in the preliminaries section as it avoids disturbance of the detailed measured work sections. This approach to preliminaries is especially critical for builders, except those using computerised systems, who produce estimates which incorporate general overheads and profit in the unit rates.

Fixed and time related costs   Fixed costs are those which do not vary with time whereas time related costs do vary with time. Take for example an item of plant, transportation to and from site involves two single costs which do not alter irrespective of whether the plant is on site for two or six weeks. Once the plant is on site the consumer cost is directly proportional to time. Thus, the time related cost element of the plant on site for two weeks will be a third of that for plant on site for six weeks.

Assessing costs in this manner not only enables more realistic prices to be established at tender but also facilitates more accurate assessment of the cost implications of preliminary items which arise from an architect's instruction to alter the works during the site production stage. Unfortunately detailed breakdowns of preliminaries prices, whether or not separated into fixed and time components, are not mandatory. However, presenting preliminaries costs as components could be advantageous to both parties.

In the case of an architect varying the work in such a way as to cause prolongation of the contract duration any subsequent assessment, of the builder's incurred prolongation costs, may be restricted to those relating to time. For the builder there is the dual benefit of receiving adequate payment for all time related preliminaries affected by any variation that prolongs the work and safeguarding any fixed cost elements in the event of the volume of work being reduced by the architect. Acceptable cost adjustments can therefore be agreed more easily and is achieved in a manner which is free of the customary disputes normally associated with such assessments. For the client there is the benefit of only having to pay for the actual cost components that are affected, thus restricting additional payments to legitimate variations in cost.

---

continued

adjusted irrespective of where the monies are allocated and further, all items where prices have not been inserted against them are deemed to be included in the tender sum and are therefore automatically subject to adjustment if affected by a variation order.

It is interesting to note that the concept of time related and fixed charges is more universally accepted within civil engineering contracts with quantities. Here, under the general heading of method related charges, provision is made within each measured work section of the BQ for CE contractors to enter a description and price for any associated time and/or cost overhead component. Unfortunately, the effectiveness of this provision is often lost due to the fact that it is again not mandatory for contractors to complete any of the method related charges sections with a BQ.

The proportion of fixed and time components within each item varies considerably. Take for example the differences between items such as hoardings, scaffolding and a tower crane, as outlined in table 8.2. It is evident from table 8.2 that hoardings consist mainly of fixed cost components and therefore are generally not affected by duration. However, it is acknowledged that the cost of adaptations and final dismantle/removal will eventually increase with time. Thus, as in this example there is often a fine dividing line between a cost which constitutes fixed as opposed to a cost which is time related.

Item	Fixed component	Time component	Main cost component
Hoardings	Purchase price, erect, adapt, remove	Maintain	Mainly fixed component
Tower crane	Transport, erect, remove, hard base, test, power supply	Hire charge, operator, power	Substantial fixed component initially but time portion increases with duration
Mixers	Transport, site preparation	Hire charge, fuel, maintain	Mainly time component

Table 8.2   Fixed and time components of preliminary items

Plant costs consist mainly of time related components as do site management costs. However, the significance of the time related component of plant items may be affected by the high cost of transporting long distances or exceptionally short hire periods or, as in the case of the tower crane, significant fixed cost components.

Fluctuations and firm price   Builders may be required to submit either a fluctuating or firm price tender. For example, these options are the subject of clauses 38 to 40 in the JCT 80 form of contract and formula rules supplement. When a fluctuating price is required the method of calculating price adjustments is either by establishing the actual changes that are incurred or by formula adjustment based on an index of national price changes. The builder must, at tender stage, be informed of the method of adjusting for fluctuations along with any restrictions on recovery that are intended to be imposed by the client beyond those stated in the form of contract.

Firm price – this relates to a fixed price contract where the prices contained in the contract bills are not adjusted to take account of fluctuations in the cost of labour (workpeople) and materials. This is, however, not strictly true as the contract does allow fluctuations and changes which arise as a direct result of government legislation, although excluding levies relating to the 1964 Industrial Training Act. For example, government may alter import duty on timber and other building materials from abroad or reintroduce the selective employment tax which was once imposed on employers for each person employed. In addition, fluctuations in the cost of electricity are allowable together with any fuels that are specified in the tender documents.[2] Because of the limited scope for price adjustment the contract is often referred to as a fixed price contract with limited fluctuations.

Thus with a firm price contract the builder must make due allowance for all price variations which will be encountered from start to finish of the contract other than those for which qualify for adjustment, likely changes in labour, material and plant costs are ascertained by projecting current trends in price and general inflation and by use of past records establish when changes may occur and which resources will be affected. Note that this approach is only an estimate of price changes and the accuracy is not only dependant upon complexity of calculations, quality of feedback and experience but also the accuracy of the net cost estimate under analysis.

All prices, other than those for prime costs, provisional sums and contingencies, but including attendances on PC sums, need to be considered. Work to be carried out by domestic sub-contractors need only be considered in situations where they are not prepared to give a firm price for the full period required.

In order to assess the likely changes that will be incurred during the contract it is necessary for builders to split their work into the respective resources of labour, materials and plant. Where applicable sub-contractors are dealt with individually. The value of each resource within the net cost estimate may be determined as a proportion of the builders work: labout 40%, materials 45% and plant 15%. Note that these given proportions are arbitrary and in practice would have to be established from feedback of previous jobs of similar type and size. Whilst this is not the most accurate method of assessing the value of resources it will provide a reasonable indication of the respective resource values very quickly.

Having completed this analysis then likely price changes for each resource can be calculated. Future changes in some of the resource costs may be known at the tender stage and can be accounted for with confidence. However, as this is not probable, except for labour increases on jobs with short contract periods, price changes have to be predicted. This relies heavily on experience and knowledge of market trends.

With sufficient time and staff available it is possible with the aid of a production programme to extract from the estimating sheets the exact monthly resource values. This will enable the actual resources included in the estimate to be considered for fluctuating costs and also at the stage in the contract that such costs are likely to be incurred. Whilst unlike the proportional approach this provides an accurate breakdown of resource costs there still remains the problem of predicting the changes that will be incurred.

Another popular approach to incorporating fluctuations into the estimate is to adjust the resource costs during pricing, thereby building the adjustment directly into each unit rate. This should not impede the pricing process but does necessitate that likely fluctuations are considered at an early stage.

The following is an example of how a firm price allowance for materials may be approximated:

Data: Tender to be submitted on 16 January
            Commencement date on 15 March
            Completion date on 15 September
            Value of materials element of tender   £15000.

The builder has predicted that prices will rise by an average of 12% over the next twelve months. From this it is anticipated that prices will rise uniformly at 1% per month. The period to be considered for increased costs purposes is from the tender date to the contract completion which in this case is eight months.

Estimate tender allowance for increased costs of materials =
£15th × 1% × 8 months
        = £1200.

This is clearly a simplistic approach for assessing fluctuations. However, more complex methods are not necessarily more accurate because they also rely on approximations. Such approximations include the likely levels of price changes, the dates when such changes will occur and the accuracy of the pre-tender construction programme to predict the actual performance on site.

Fluctuating price – this relates to a fixed price contract where the prices are adjusted to take account of fluctuations which occur after the date of tender. The cost variations may be calculated by either a non formula or a formula method, whichever is stated in the particular tender documents.

Non formula method

Commonly referred to as full fluctuations this method allows for the changes in the prices contained in the contract bills of labour, materials, electricity and fuels, where stated, which occur after the date of tender. However, all price changes promulgated (declaration of agreement) prior to the date of tender must be included in the tender price irrespective of when such changes actually take place during the contract. In this context the date of tender, now referred to as the base date, is inserted in the JCT 80 form of contract appendix by the client – by stating the number of days prior to the date of submission. In the JCT 63 form the date of tender for fluctuations calculations is defined as ten days prior to the tender submission date. These arrangements are to avoid constant changes to the estimate in the event that numerous notifications of price increases are issued to tenderers in the final few days of the tender period.

The labour costs contained in the contract sum which are subject to fluctuations include rates of wages fixed by the National Joint Council for the Building Industry (NJCBI) or other recognised wage fixing body. The JCT 80 form of contract provides that where such wages are used then any incentive scheme, which conforms to the incentive scheme rules of any associated wage fixing body, are also allowable for fluctuations adjustment. In addition, JCT 80 also provides for fluctuations in travelling costs which are incurred by the builder in respect of workpeople. This includes the cost of transport provided for workpeople for which the builder has listed and submitted with his tender and/or for the reimbursement of fares to workpeople in accordance with NJCBI rules.

The term *workpeople* refers to operatives employed in connection with the work either on or adjacent the site and those directly employed off site by the builder to produce materials or goods for the works. This includes supervisors or the like (non workperson) in so far as they are physically carrying out the work of a workperson. In such circumstances a supervisor is classed as a workperson for the time engaged in physical work. Note that whilst the workpeople of domestic sub-contractors are included for fluctuations purposes this is not the case with labour-only sub-contractors. Labour only sub-contractors are excluded as their wages are not set by a recognised wage-fixing body such as the NJCBI which deals with building operatives such as joiners, bricklayers and labourers.

As regards materials and goods there are a number of procedures which have to be complied with in order that price variations qualify for adjustment under this particular fluctuations clause:

- Each material required by the builder to be the subject of fluctuations, including those of domestic sub-contractors, must be entered on a basic prices list, figure 8.1, and submitted with the tender.
- The basic cost is deemed to be the net cost after the deduction of trade discounts and a price change relates to the change in the market price. Monthly account (MA) discounts are incentives for early payment and do not affect fluctuations calculations whether included or not.
- During the contract the QS requires proof of price changes. Thus the quotations used to produce the tender price and subsequent invoices must be provided for comparison. Note that prices contained in quotations should match those on the basic prices list. The treatment of monthly account (cash) discounts must also be consistent between quotations and invoices. However, quotations for certain materials such as cement may not be obtained at tender due to the common usage on site, especially if bought in bulk for later distribution. In such cases invoices received prior to tender should serve as evidence in place of a quotation.
- Prices on the basic price list for materials are deemed to be for full load deliveries unless otherwise stated. If part load quotations are not included on the list the adjustment for an increase relating to a part load delivery can still be considered but the invoiced amount would be substituted for a current full load price.

Material	Unit	Basic price delivered to site
Sand	tonne	£10
Cement	tonne	£60
Bricks and blocks		As per quote from Good Price Brick Supplies Ltd dated 4 May 1990*

* It is common practice to list all the brick and block types along with their associated prices. However, there is no advantage in preparing lists in such a time consuming manner.

Figure 8.1   List of basic prices of materials and goods

Because materials have to be purchased from the same source as that used in the tender sum, in order that a builder can claim for fluctuations, this not only limits the choice of supplier but also limits the choice of domestic sub-contractors to those used at the tender stage. The system therefore gives the builder little incentive to improve on the buying and sub-letting arrangements to which he is initially rushed into arranging. This is due to the time constrains imposed by unrealistic tender periods. Such a situation cannot be beneficial to either party to the contract.

Unfortunately, it is not always possible to use the same supplier, or more commonly the same sub-contractor, as that used to prepare the tender. This may be due to a number of circumstances outside the control of the builder. For instance a sub-contractor may recently have ceased trading or the builder has since entered into litigation with a sub-contractor which has compromised further working relationships. These situations are usually treated sympathetically by the QS when properly presented.

The following is an example of how a promulgated labour increase may be approximated for inclusion in a tender for a contract with full fluctuations:

Data: Tender to be submitted on 16 January
              Commencement date on 15 March
              Completion date on 15 September
              Value of labour element of tender   £12000.
              Base date is ten days before submission

An increase in operatives wages was promulgated on 2 January and the builder received notification of the agreement on 4 January. The increase represented a 10% addition on operatives wages, to take effect from 1 June.

The timing of these events is as follows:

As promulgation occurs prior to the base date the labour increases are subject to adjustment and the period to be considered for increased costs purposes is from 1 June to 15 September, which in this case is 3.5 months.

Assuming the labour requirements are similar for each month

the estimated tender allowance for increased costs of labour =
£12th × 10% × 3.5 months
6
= £700.

A more accurate assessment is possible by calculating the anticipated number of labour hours included in the estimate for work after the month of May.

Whilst the fluctuations provision is fairly comprehensive in terms of labour and materials recovery there is still a significant proportion of the contract that is excluded. This includes materials omitted from the list, plant including consumable stores and small tools, labour only sub-contractors, spot bonuses and other bonuses not conforming to working rule agreements, management staff, overheads and profit. It is worth noting that whilst such items as scaffold and hoardings, including timber for hoardings, are treated as plant any timbers used for formwork are classified as materials and should therefore be included on the materials list for fluctuations.

The cost implications of the shortfall in fluctuations recovery may be calculated for each job based on the individual assessment of each component. Alternatively, a much speedier method is to make a lump sum adjustment to the tender sum. This is by way of a percentage addition, the size of which is based on a combination of experience together with feedback from previous contracts.

Builders must be aware of the relevant conditions which relate to each form of contract in respect of the implementation of fluctuations involving work carried out after the completion date (or that date extended by the architect). In essence the implications are that fluctuations only continue after the completion date where the method of adjustment is by formula although in such cases the index to be used for adjustment is that which is the last index falling within the contract period (or revised). The inflationary index is thus frozen.[3] However, these changes to the implementation of the three fluctuations options are void and therefore cannot be enforced in either of two circumstances:

Amendments have been made to JCT 80 clauses 25.4.10.1 and/or 2, extension of time for relevant events concerning the builder's inability to obtain labour and materials respectively which could not have been foreseen at tender and either clause 38.4.8.1 (limited) or 39.5.8.1. (full) or 40.7.2.1 (formula), as applicable, have not been deleted.

The position with nominated sub-contractors in respect of fluctuations is similar to that of the main contractor although the issue of terminating or freezing such adjustments is centred around the date of completion of a specific nominated sub-contract rather than that of the main contract date of completion. Also, under

NSC/4 or 4a there is provision for an addition of one thirty-ninth to all fluctuations calculations so that the contractual 2.5% builder's discount is maintained on the whole of the nominated sub-contractor's account.

The main drawback with the non formula method of fluctuations recovery is that the processing of data for payment is very time consuming. This is exasperated in situations where such data is not available at the time required. Both result in delays in data processing which in turn leads to delayed payments to the builder. Delayed payments on costs already incurred automatically have an adverse affect on the project cash flow and in particular the builder's working capital requirements. Thus, the affects of such cash shortfalls may have to be considered at the tender stage.

Formula method

This method is based on a number of price indices issued monthly by the Department of the Environment (DoE). The change in index which takes place from one month to the next is obtained from the published indices and expressed as a percentage of the base index stated in the contract. In essence, the percentage is then multiplied by the work completed during the monthly period in order to determine the value of fluctuations adjustment. The process is repeated each month to provide the builder with up to date payments for costs incurred.

The calculations are actually more extensive than that outlined in so much as a different index is used for each part of the work. The parts of the work are in accordance with either Part 1 or 2 of the Formula Rules, whichever the contract specifies. Part 1 requires indices to be applied to their respective Work Categories. Series 2 provides 49 possible categories, for example, 2/1 is demolitions, 2/2 is excavations. . . , 2/3 is hardcore and fill. Part 2 concerns Work Groups, these being made up of combinations of work categories, for example, 2/1 to 2/3 may be grouped together. Where work is grouped together the value of that work is adjusted monthly using an aggregated index derived from the weighted indices of the individual work categories.

Thus the formula method of fluctuations adjustment facilitates notional changes in the market prices of labour, materials and plant as opposed to those which are actually incurred. The price changes are notional in that they are based on average national price changes obtained from manufacturers that supply the industry. Therefore, resultant regional and local price changes are likely to be different.

The notional price levels are represented numerically by a series of indices which fluctuate in line with changing market prices. Each index is made up of both labour and material elements which are weighted in order to reflect the actual price change of the work it covers. As only a limited number of indices are used to represent the numerous price related items each index comprises of a basket of related items each of which fluctuate in price at different levels. For example, work category 2/11, brickwork and blockwork, is represented by one index. However, there are numerous types and sizes of bricks together with many different brick manufacturers, not to mention the various types of building blocks. Because of the differences in price changes between each of these it is inevitable that a specific price change experienced by any builder is never exactly the same as that represented by the index. Such differences are obviously magnified when Part 2 Work Group is used.

It is worth noting that these work categories are not used on all contracts. For instance, the Property Services Agency produce their own standard work groups for use on GC/works/1.

Balance of adjustable work

This relates to that part of the contract sum where work which is not covered by a work category or treated as specialist work, with the exception of items specifically excluded by the formula rules. Such work is adjusted by the same percentage as that which represents the total value of the adjusted work. Thus, in order to calculate the percentage adjustment on the balance of adjustable work the total value of the fluctuations calculated for the adjusted work is expressed as a percentage of the value of the adjusted work.

DoE published indices

The DoE monthly indices for any specific month are understandably produced after the month end. Thus, to provide continuity in adjustments the DoE include provisional indices until such time as firm (updated) indices are produced. This means that for example the September indices publication includes a column of provisional incides for that month and another column that contains the firm indices for June. Fluctuations calculations are therefore initially based on provisional data and later recalculated using confirmed data.

Adjustments for under or over recovery

The builder must make all due allowances in his tender for any under or over recovery that may result from fluctuations by formula method. Feedback from previous jobs is very important when making such decisions. In this respect specific attention must be given to both imported goods, such as sanitary fittings manufactured in Italy, and any specified non-adjustable element stated in JCT 80 local authority contract conditions:

goods manufactured abroad – goods manufactured outside the UK, which are to be directly incorporated into the works are excluded from the formula adjustment. These goods may be dealt with as prime cost sums – this is because a builder's firm price allowance may be greater than the actual increase costs incurred. Alternatively the builder may include the imported goods on a basic price list, the price of which is given as the pound sterling equivalent. In such cases the price changes are dealt with on a full fluctuations basis.

non-adjustable element – is a specified percentage of the work, not exceeding 10%, which is not subject to fluctuations adjustment. As the non-adjustable percentage applies to the total contract sum and not specific sections thereof the reduction is applied to each work group or category value. Note that the estimator must calculate the non-adjustable element value and allow for this in the tender sum.

In general, builder's favour this method of fluctuations adjustment as it allows up to date adjustments to be made speedily on each monthly valuation. Further, allowances for any shortfalls in recovery can be adequately catered for at tender stage through the use of feedback from other jobs.

References

1 GRAY, C, 'Estimating preliminaries' Part 1: 'Looking at the problems', *Building Technology and Management*, April 1983, pp 4, 5.
2 JCT, *Standard form of building contract*, Part 3: 'Fluctuations' (clause 37 refers), Fluctuation clauses for use with private editions with, without and with approximate quantities, RIBA 1980, pp 1–2.
3 PARRIS, J, *The standard form of building contract* JCT 80, Second edition, Collins 1985, pp 164–166.

Questions

1 Use examples to distinguish between the assessment of plant costs in:
   (i) the measured work sections of a bill of quantities (see also Chapter 5.)
   (ii) the overheads schedule.

2 For a traditional procurement arrangement:
   (a) Discuss the function of the preliminaries section of a bill of quantities (see also Chapter 4.)
   (b) Explain the procedure for pricing project overheads and their incorporation in the priced bill of quantities (see also Chapter 7.)

3 Explain the benefits of the following estimating procedures:
   (a) the building-up of a project overheads schedule with separate calculations for fixed charges and time-related costs
   (b) the analytical pricing of items of work in a bill of quantities (see also Chapter 3.)

9 General Overheads and Profit

A tender sum consists of the net cost estimate plus an addition for overheads and profit. In this context these two elements are commonly referred to collectively as either gross profit or mark-up or margin. However, whilst mark-up is often applied as a single item due to the distinct differences between the two elements each need to be considered separately. The responsibility for determining mark-up is that of management, at the adjudication meeting.

General overheads These are the costs associated with running a company, as opposed to those required to support individual projects, and are often referred to as head office charges or overheads. As with project overheads these costs must be fully recovered by the builder, from projects that are carried out. General overheads generally include:

directors' and office staff salaries, including employers pension contributions, medical insurance, etc

upkeep of offices, central storage facilities and other out buildings together with the land within the confines of the property, rent, rates and maintenance costs

services, such as telephones, heating, lighting and liability insurance

finance costs such as a bank overdraft – most builders operated with an overdraft

cars and other vehicles including maintenance and depreciation.

Note that any other costs which the builder does not wish to specifically allocate to individual projects need to be included in the general overheads. This may include small tools, vans, lorries, general plant items such as a water pump, central storage facilities and the like, these being made available for use by any site. Further, where professionals such as surveyors, contracts managers and particularly planners are not site based it may be more expedient to also include these functions (cost centres) in the overhead calculations rather than trying to account for them individually on the merits of each project.

Quantification of general overheads   Each builder has a unique set of general overheads and as a consequence will incur a different cost to that of competitors. As the normal scope for competition between builders in tendering situations is limited to sequence/method, project overheads, margin and in many instances time, ie speed of erection, it is in the interests of each builder to maintain general overhead costs at the lowest possible level due to its competitive element. In this respect general overheads are therefore very similar to project overheads and therefore need to be kept under control and constantly reviewed.

In order to meet these costs the required revenue can only be acquired from projects carried out, assuming that building contracting is the only source of revenue for the organisation. This is achieved in general terms by adding a proportion of the total overhead requirement to each project. The proportion is established by expressing overheads as a percentage of turnover. Both the overheads and turnover values used may be either those recorded from the previous financial year or alternatively the respective figures projected to meet the targets for the year commencing.

Because the general overheads addition is applied to the net cost estimates then it follows that the derived percentage is calculated on the same basis. A typical calculation is shown in figure 9.1. This simplistic view of the process provides an explanation of the general principles involved in establishing the general overheads addition.

	£m	
Gross turnover	10.00	Gen o/heads as a proportion of net
Less Profit	.30	cost (turnover) =
	9.70	$\dfrac{0.65}{9.05}$ x 100%
Less Gen o/heads	.65	= 7.18%
net annual cost	9.05	=====

(not 6.5% ie $\dfrac{0.65 \text{x} 100}{10.00}$)

Figure 9.1   Calculation of the general overheads percentage

Assessment of general overheads   Although general overheads are expressed as a percentage, as shown in figure 9.1, there are other factors such as contribution and success ratio which may influence the actual level of general overheads applied to any specific project. These considerations are not divorced from the issues associated with bidding strategy.

Contribution here refers to the extent to which total overheads are recovered from a specific project. For instance, a project valued at £1m with a duration of twelve months will contribute twice the amount towards total annual overheads than the same project with a duration of twelve months. However, this would only affect the overhead recovery for the year if overall turnover for the year is not achieved.

Success ratio relates to the number of successful bids. This influences the extent to which the total general overheads of an organisation are recovered. For example, if more jobs than anticipated are won, assuming each is of the usual size, value and level of contribution for the organisation, then general overheads are recovered early in the trading cycle.

In such a situation the builder may decide to maintain the bid policy as long as this does not lead to overtrading (insufficient funds to finance the increased turnover). The additional revenue generated, less any marginal increases in costs, would provide extra profit. Alternatively the builder may wish to keep the annual turnover at the level planned for the year. This can be achieved by either reducing the number of bids or increasing the applied overheads. By increasing the overheads the builder will still achieve increased profits if the planned turnover is maintained. Another option for the builder is to reduce turnover in order to maintain the planned level of general overheads.

These considerations are taken a little further in the following example:

A builder has a planned turnover of £10m based on an average equivalent of ten jobs undertaken per annum. The equivalent value per annum of each job is £1m. A bid is to be submitted for a job which has an annual equivalent value of £2m. The builder is able to cope with any additional turnover that may result from this bid being successful.

Here, assuming the job is desirable there are a number of options open to the builder:

- increase turnover by now undertaking eleven jobs (£12m)
- increase turnover by undertaking ten jobs including the £2m contract (£11m)
- maintain turnover by undertaking only nine jobs (£10m)

The two options for increased turnover provide scope for the builder to either chance winning the £2m contract with the normal addition for general overheads, thus increasing possible profit or increase the probability of winning by reducing the level of applied overheads, thereby becoming more competitive.

Unfortunately not all builders find themselves in the enviable position of high success ratios and high mark-ups. Where the market is more aggressive builders may be in a position where planned turnover is difficult to achieve. It is hard to correct this situation by simply increasing the applied overheads on a reduced number of jobs as this only makes the builder less competitive.

The options here are either to attempt to win more jobs by intensifying bidding or seek less competitive work. If planned turnover is still unattainable a riskier option is to reduce the level of applied overheads in the hope of winning more jobs. By taking this option the builder must also either take on a greater number of jobs or increase the value of individual jobs undertaken to meet the annual overhead requirement. Both alternatives involve increased turnover and therefore are likely to have wider implications for overheads. It is therefore necessary for builders to monitor regularly the organisations performance in order to react to new situations as they arise.

Net profit   Net profit is the difference between revenue and cost. Therefore, after an organisation has paid all costs incurred in running the business, any excess monies is the achieved profit (before tax). Calculating the amount of profit for tendering purposes, figures 9.2, is on the same basis as that outlined for general overheads in figure 9.1. However, whilst the considerations for assessing the level of profit to be apportioned to a job are basically the same as those for general overheads it must be remembered that generally the net profit is additional to and not part of the elements within a tender sum which are necessary to ensure cost recovery.

	£m	
Gross turnover	10.00	Net profit as a
		proportion of net
Less Profit	.30	cost (turnover) =
	9.70	$\dfrac{0.30}{9.05} \times 100\%$
Less Gen o/heads	.65	
		= 3.32%
net annual cost	9.05	=====
		(not 3.0% ie $\dfrac{0.30 \times 100}{10.00}$)

Figure 9.2   Calculation of the net profit percentage

In certain circumstances the net profit may have to supplement the cost contribution of other elements within the tender sum. For instance, where the actual costs are greater than anticipated costs then the achieved net profit is reduced by the shortfall. Assuming that during the contract there is no scope for improving profit, if the applied net profit is greater than the shortfall then the achieved profit for the job will be the difference between the applied net profit and the shortfall. Here, the builder will achieve a reduced profit on the job.

Where the shortfall is greater than the applied net profit then the net profit element will be lost. Further, the full cost of general overheads will not be covered. Here, the builder will make a loss on the job.

Thus, the only element of a tender sum that allows scope for adjustment without foreseeably affecting cost recovery is the net profit addition. It is because of this that whilst both elements of the mark-up may be considered in conjunction with each other the net profit is the foremost element to be adjusted.

Profitability   Whilst profit constitutes a measure of a company's financial achievement in relation to the total business turnover it is not a conclusive measure of financial performance. For instance, two identical builders may each achieve a 1% profit on a turnover of £1000m (US billion). However, the first builder may have achieved the profit level by incurring a working capital requirement (capital employed) of £30m whereas the second builder's working capital requirement is £50m. Investors would therefore be more interested in the first company as opposed to the second.

Profitability is a measure which takes account of the level of capital employed:

$$\frac{\text{Profit}}{\text{Capital employed}} \times 100\%$$

Thus, the financial performance of the two organisations is:

first builder achieves 30% profitability
second builder achieves 20% profitability

Alternatively, statements of net current assets from each company's balance sheets may be used to establish the performance of each organisation. Note that the difference between an organisation's current assets and current liabilities is the total working capital requirement. Current assets and current liabilities may also be used as an indicant of performance, in the form of the current ratio. Thus, if a company has current assets of £100m and current liabilities of £50m then the current ratio is 2 to 1, this representing a good ratio. However, if the current liabilities were greater than £100m, say £120m, then the company with a current ratio of .83 to 1 is likely to be financially ruined.

Allocating mark-up   Having established the level of mark-up to be applied to the job the next step is to decide where this sum of money is to be included in the overall tender sum. There are a number of different ways in which this sum may be allocated within a bill of quantities, some being easy to implement and others more difficult. However, the allocation of the sum is left entirely to the builder's discretion:

Lump sum addition – The easiest way of allocating mark-up to a BQ is to add it as either a lump sum or percentage addition. The addition is made either to the total net cost summary or, if in the form of a lump sum, may be hidden within the preliminaries section.

Distribution throughout all sections – This involves increasing all prices within the BQ to the value of the mark-up by proportions. One practice is to distribute the mark-up proportionally throughout the bill. Here, each price is increased by the mark-up percentage. Another practice is to have a disproportionate distribution of the mark-up. This involves allocating differing amounts to different parts of the bill. Disproportionate distribution is therefore more complicated than spreading the mark-up evenly through the BQ.

However, both practices are too time consuming for any builder to attempt at the end of the tender period unless the estimate has been prepared on a computer which has an appropriate facility for allocation. Where computers are used an alternative to adjusting the rates and prices is to adjust the price of work to be carried out by others in conjunction with making disproportionate adjustments to the individual resource costs (labour, materials, plant) contained in the builder's own work item prices.

Distribution throughout selected sections – This practice involves either proportionate or disproportionate distribution, as outlined above, of the total mark-up value throughout the selected parts of the estimate, whether they be bill prices, individual resources or a mixture of each. The practice of loading selected sections is as problematic as that for the loading of all sections unless limited to simple lump sum additions to a few individual items.

Adjustment for balance of any mark-up included in the rates – As many builders add their mark-up to individual rates as they are generated during the estimating process, the total value included is likely to be more or less that required by management. Thus the balance is usually added or subtracted as a lump sum from the preliminaries section.

Question
Describe the information required by management to convert an estimate to a tender.

10 Cash Flow Forecasting

Purpose of cash flow forecasting Cash flow (CF) is a statement of the relationship between income and expenditure over time. Such statements are used for financial planning and control. Thus, individual cash flow forecasts (CFFs) need to be prepared for each contract and these subsequently contribute to the preparation of a builder's overall CFF.

The company CFF is not only used for financial planning internally but also used to convince banks of the organisation's current and future financial viability. This is important in order to both maintain or increase bank credit facilities and secure additional loan arrangements on occasions when the builder's own funds are insufficient. Note that in addition to bank loans and the like as a means of raising additional finance other options may be available such as share issues and debentures.

Individual contract CFs are necessary to monitor the financial performance of production in addition to establishing achieved profit levels and working capital requirements.

The purpose of cash flow forecasting for individual jobs is therefore two fold:

- At adjudication it is necessary to provide senior management with an indication of both the level of finance required during the production period and the stage at which finance is no longer required. This information is taken into consideration by management when determining the tender sum.
- Post contract it is necessary to provide site management with an accurate statement of both the level and rate of planned expenditure in order to control production costs, produce periodic performance reports to senior management and assess productivity performance levels.

In a situation where there is no provision for stage payments within a contract the builder would complete the whole of the work before receiving payment. Thus, the profit is realised in the final payment. Here, the builder would have to finance the whole of the work, therefore his working capital requirement is approximately equal to the contract sum less the mark-up – assuming that achieved costs are equal to those estimated.

However, building contracts normally have an arrangement whereby the builder is paid at agreed intervals during the contract, either at completed stages of the work or on a monthly basis. The recovery of profit is therefore achieved in stages by way of the mark-up contained within the work that is included in each valuation. Further, as the builder's credit arrangements with suppliers and sub-contractors are normally such that their payments are made after receipt of his interim payments from the client the outflow of monies is delayed, therefore improving the cash flow. As the cash flow is improved the level of finance (working capital) required to carry out the contract is reduced.

It is normal for builders to experience a cash deficit for most of the contract period. Therefore, any shortfall must be provided by the builder. As the working capital, needed to cover the shortfall, is likely to be borrowed it is vital that the job becomes self financing as soon as possible. The amount of finance required at any one time is the difference between the contract value of work done, after deducting retention, and the actual cost of carrying out the work. This is likely to fluctuate between each valuation period as the supplier/sub-contractor demand changes. Thus, the working capital requirement is likely to increase during periods when the builder's own labour intensive activity is at its highest due to the fact that operatives are paid weekly.

Discounted cash flow   As the relative value of money is eroded over time then future payments based on current prices have less value than at present. Such a phenomenon is fundamental to payment arrangements associated with building contracts and is of particular importance when projects are of long duration. In order to evaluate the capital requirement of a job the effects of stage payments must be considered. Thus, all revenue has to be converted to a common date. This is achieved by applying discounting techniques.

There are a number of methods available,[1] each of which enables the current value of each future payment to be calculated. For example, net present value (NPV) and present value of one pound (Year's Purchase) both directly produce discounted future payment values. Other methods, such as amount of one pound (compound interest), which produce future values may also be used as the methods are interchangeable, but do however require a further calculation. For example, if the future value of one pound is calculated to be £1.50 then any revenue received at that point in the future has a current value of the revenue amount divided by 1.5.

Whilst some builders may wish to apply discounting techniques this type of analysis is more likely to be undertaken by consultants when advising clients on the viability of individual developments. However, irrespective of what is to be discounted there is a major problem when attempting to apply the technique too far into the

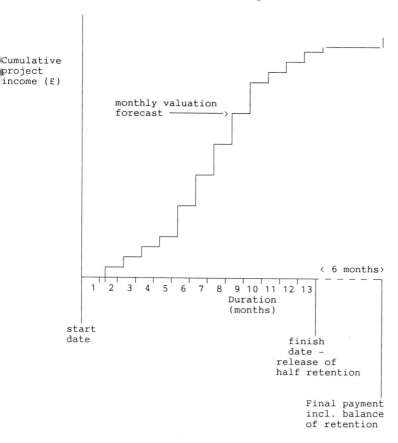

Figure 10.1   Cumulative income diagram

future. The problem arises out of the inability to predict accurately future interest rates. This is also a short term problem during periods where frequent interest rate changes are taking place. Where interest rates cannot be predicted with confidence a sensitivity analysis should be carried out in order to provide a better basis for decision making. This involves calculating alternative discounted values, using different interest rates, to establish the significance of each solution.

Characteristics of a cumulative cash flow diagram   Cash flow forecasting involves producing a budget which can then be monitored by the builder during production. The information may be presented in tabular format or graphically using either cumulative or non cumulative data. The common way to present cash flow is graphically in the form of an income/expenditure curve, based on cumulative monthly sums of money which reflect the production output in terms of cost and value over time.[2] Because site production generally starts slowly, continues at a faster rate for the major part of the contract and then finally slows down to the end of the job, a cumulative cash flow generally takes the form of an S curve, the outline of which can be seen by connecting the upper points of the stepped payments, featured in figure 10.1, with a continuous line. Note that the revenue curve does not have to be shown on the diagram as being stepped.

The steep gradient in the middle part of the curve together with the shallower gradients at either side constitute the characteristics of an S curve. In addition to the revenue curve a cumulative cash flow diagram would also contain curves representing gross and net value. Note that a cost (net value) curve starts immediately the job commences whereas the revenue curve starts later, on receipt of the first payment from the client.

Note that for the client the cash flow for the building work is a negative mirror image of the builder's stepped revenue curve.

Figure 10.2   Revenue histogram: Normal Distribution

By presenting monthly revenue or cost as a histogram, figure 10.2, a normal distribution curve is produced. However, due to the nature of building projects the histogram is more likely to have at least two peaks, one produced by the intensity of work required to complete the superstructure and the other for the internal work. The relative size of each peak depends on the nature of the job. Those jobs with a high content of services and/or lavish finishings may produce similar peaks to those shown in figure 10.3.

Further, exceptionally high peaks may also be produced when items of high value are brought onto site, eg delivery of steel frame, as figure 10.4 demonstrates. In situations where bimodality and exceptionally high peaks occur the S curve becomes distorted, the extent of which depends on the particulars of each individual project.

Figure 10.3   Revenue histogram: Bimodal Distribution

Figure 10.4   Revenue histogram: Bimodal Distribution combined with an exceptionally high peak

Monthly cash flow diagram   This diagram is produced to show the cash surplus or deficit of a project, on a monthly basis. The deficits represent working capital requirements and the surpluses indicate periods when the project is self financing. The information required to prepare a cash flow are as follows:

payment periods

contract period

retention value

value of work completed at each stage

defects liability period

details of mark-up allocation

details of delayed payment to sub-contractors and suppliers

value of delayed payments at each stage.

An example of how the monthly working capital requirements may be calculated using an S curve for forecasted gross valuations is as follows:

contract value: £250,000

contract period: six months

mark-up: 15%, added to every bill price

valuations: monthly, settled within 14 days of certification

retention: 5%

defects liability period: six months.

All payments to suppliers and sub-contractors are after main contractors payment whilst payments to operatives are weekly, monthly values are given in table 10.1.

Note that all subsequent values in this example are assumed.

Month	Gross value of delayed payments (£)	Net value of delayed payments (£)
1	20000	17391
2	32000	27826
3	41000	35652
4	45000	39130
5	35000	30434
6	22000	19130

Table 10.1   Value of anticipated delayed payments to creditors

Forecasted cumulative and monthly gross valuations are obtained from the S curve. The net cost values are then subsequently derived for each month, as shown in table 10.2.

Month	cumulative gross value (£)	monthly gross value (£)	monthly net cost (£) *
1	25000	25000	21739
2	73000	48000	41739
3	123000	50000	43478
4	178000	55000	47826
5	223000	45000	39130
6	250000	27000	23478

* As net cost plus 15% mark-up = gross value, the monthly cost is as $\dfrac{\text{monthly value}}{115\%}$

Table 10.2   Anticipated revenue and cost

The cash flow figures are now calculated (excluding adjustments for sub-contractors' retentions) and the results displayed diagrammatically in figure 10.5.

```
                                                        Deficit (-)/
                                                        surplus (+)
Month 1
week 4                    net cost          21739
               Ddt net delayed
                          payment 1         17391
                          (weekly costs)     4348       -  4348 max
                          Ddt revenue          -
                                             4348       -  4348 min
Month 2
week 6         net cost          41739
               Ddt del pay 2     27826
               (weekly costs)    13913/2      6957
                                             11305      - 11305 max
          Ddt revenue
          (valuation 1)    25000
          less retention    1250            23750
                                           +12445      + 12445 min
week 8                    Add del pay 1     17391
                                             4946
                          Weekly costs       6956
                                            11902
Month 3
week 10        net cost          43478
               Ddt del pay 3     35652
               (wkly costs)       7826/2      3913
                                             15815      - 15815 max
          Ddt revenue
          (val 2)          48000
          less ret          2400            45600
                                           +29785      + 29785 min
week 12                   Add del pay 2     27826
                                           + 1959
                          weekly costs       3913
                                             1954
Month 4
week 14        net cost          47826
               Ddt del pay 4     39130
               (wkly costs)       8696/2      4348
                                             6302       -  6302 max
          Ddt revenue
          (val 3)          50000
          less ret          2500            47500
                                           +41198      + 41198 min
week 16                   Add del pay 3     35652
                                           + 5546
                          weekly costs       4348
                                           + 1198
Month 5
week 18        net cost          39130
               Ddt del pay 5     30434
               (wkly costs)       8696/2      4348
                                             3150       -  3150 max
```

continued overleaf

```
            Ddt revenue
            (val 4)           55000
            less ret           2750         52250
                                           +49100      + 49100 min
week 20                Add del pay 4        39130
                                           + 9970
                       weekly costs          4348
                                           + 5622
Month 6
week 22     net cost          23478
            Ddt del pay 6      19130
            (wkly costs)        4348/2       2174
                                           + 3448      +  3448 max
            Ddt revenue
            (val 5)           45000
            less ret           2250         42750
                                           +46198      + 46198 min
week 24                Add del pay 5        30434
                                           +15764
                       weekly costs          2174
                                           +13590
Month 7
week 26                net cost                -
                                           +13590


            Ddt revenue
            (val 6 = penultimate)           27000
                                           +40590
            half retention release
            (2.5% of cum gross val
            at month 5 = £223000
            OR  £11150 )                     5575
                    2                        46165      + 46165 max
week 28                Add del pay 6        19130
                                           +27035      + 27035 min

Month 13
Assume week 50
            Release balance of retention
            (Final payment)                  5575
                                           +32610      + 32610 max/min
                                                       (gross profit)
```

Note that whilst in theory the final payment is the balance of retention, in practice there are usually monies outstanding from the main account. The payment of retention balance is dependent on how soon the builder makes good any defects that occur during the six months after completion of the works. Further, the final payment depends on how soon the final account is settled. Thus, such payments are likely to occur after month 13.

Detailed forecasting Detailed cash flow forecasts are formulated from an accurate production programme, the values of which are taken from the estimate. This process involves abstracting from the programme all the activities and parts thereof which are shown to take place each month. The value of these activities are then calculated using the prices contained in the estimate. Cost/revenue

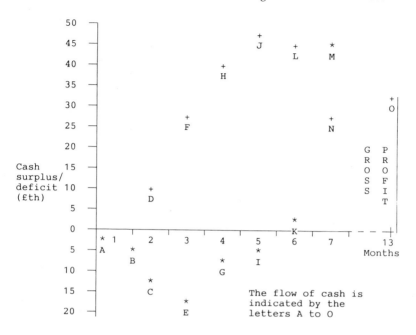

Figure 10.5   Monthly cash flow diagram with delayed payments to creditors

curves and monthly cash flow diagrams may then be produced. The adjustments for delayed payments, retention and the like are as detailed for the preparation of the monthly cash flow diagram.

If activities within the programme contain float then this may be taken into account. If float is not to be taken into account then the cash flow is calculated using the earliest start dates (front end programme). This results in a single S curve. Where float is to be accounted for then the cash flow calculations need to be carried out twice. The first set of calculations will incorporate the earliest start date of each activity and the second calculations will incorporate the latest start date. This will result in two S curves running side by side although each share the same start and end point. Together the curves take a form similar to that of a pea pod. When monitoring costs during production the actual or probable cumulative curve should fall within the two predicted curves. If the actual curve follows the left of the two curves then production is shown to be high whereas if it moves outside the confines of the two curves, to the right, then the job may need reprogramming.

Thus, if a detailed cash flow is to be produced during the tender stage then it is important that an accurate programme is available early enough to allow adequate time to prepare the forecast. However, due to the difficulties of both producing an accurate programme and maintaining progress on site it is unlikely that the cash flow forecast will be an exact representation of the achieved cash flow. Further, it is advisable to check that the prices contained in the estimate have not been distorted through disproportionate distribution of gross profit and the like. Details of such adjustments need to be recorded and taken into account in any calculations in order to produce a realistic cash flow forecast.

Approximate forecasting methods   As programmes are not either accurate or always available at the tender stage other methods must be adopted in order to produce a cash flow. These methods allow experienced practitioners to produce reasonable results very quickly and with little effort. The approximate methods include notional S curves and mathematical formulae:

S curves

There are a number of ways in which to produce a notional S curve, the most reliable is by interpolating recorded S curves of past jobs of a similar nature, type, size and value.

Another approach is by the quarter/third curve. Here, it is assumed that the one quarter of the value is achieved at one third of the contract period and three quarters of the value is achieved at two thirds of the contract period. By marking these two points on a cumulative value to time graph a line is drawn from zero and continued through the two points and extended to the contract value/completion date intersection. This is a best fit line that should give a curve in the form of an S.

An alternative is the half/third curve. This assumes that one third of the value is achieved half way through the contract. However, the gradients at the top and bottom of the S curve are completely subjective due to the absence of strategically placed points of reference.

Formulae

A number of mathematical formulae have been devised to produce S curves, the most renowned in the building industry being the DHSS (Department of Health and Social Security) equation. However, one problem found to be inherent within the DHSS equation is that when applied to certain projects the early part of the builder's cumulative cost/revenue curve is shown as a negative flow. Equations should therefore be well tested before organisations rely on them too much.

Improving cash flow   Cash flow may be improved by actions taken at both the tender stage and post contract.

At tender stage

Improving cash flow is achieved by either front or back end loading of the prices which form the estimate. However, the practice of loading is risky and may result in the builder losing more money than he stands to gain:

Front end loading – This involves a disproportionate distribution of gross profit in such a manner as to secure recovery at an early stage of the work. An extreme example of this practice is where the whole of the gross profit is distributed throughout the substructure section. To improve the situation even further it is also possible to take money off some of the rates at the end of the job and again add it into the substructure items. This would result in the builder recovering the whole of the mark-up for the job, in a short period of time, together with some of the value of later work. These early payments would fund the running of the project at the client's expense. Further, this represents a financial risk to the client should the builder become bankrupt soon after the substructures are completed.

Front end loading is not recommended as good practice and, further, presents the builder with some risk. *Firstly*, if on inspection of tenders the QS suspects front end loading then the client will be advised to reject the bid. However, it is difficult to spot such loading if practised by all bidders. Further, the QS's own cost calculations may also be equally distorted if his cost data is based on loaded bids. *Secondly*, if the architect revises the drawings in such a manner as to substantially reduce that part of the work which has been loaded, in this case the substructures, then the builder will lose the proportion of mark-up allocated to the reductions.

Back end loading – This is the reverse of front end loading whereby monies are taken from the front of the job and allocated at the back.

This is suitable on long duration contracts which have a formula fluctuations clause. The intention is to forfeit early payments for later payments which will attract high fluctuation indices. This is the same as keeping monies back from a valuation for inclusion in the next valuation in the knowledge that the following fluctuation index will increase rapidly – due to significant increases in current resource costs which are known to be taking effect before or during that next valuation period.

To implement back end loading successfully the builder must be sure that the extra monies acquired outweigh the additional cost of funding the job. However, it is very difficult to predict this with certainty due to the instability of both interest rates and levels of inflation.

Post contract

At this stage cash flow may be improved by ensuring that all monies due to the builder are claimed and subsequently received immediately and that potential losses are avoided:

- accurate valuations are taken at the prescribed intervals and on time. Valuations should include monies for all variations (including dayworks) completed, increased costs, claims for loss and expense. Where approximate/provisional figures have been used in valuations these must be substituted by accurate figures as soon as they are available
- all entitlements to extensions of the contract period are obtained
- retentions are released without delay and the final account is settled on time
- credit control to ensure payments to the builder are received on time and monies long overdue are recovered, especially old accounts where retentions and final payments may have been delayed due to a technicality
- obtain maximum credit facilities from both suppliers and sub-contractors. Better discounts/prices may be negotiated but that may undermine the competitiveness of future quotations.
- improve cost and quality control.

Cost and production control   Site management are responsible for production within both time and cost constraints. Because of the problems associated with production the site manager is constantly required to answer the following questions:

- why is the contract in front of programme but losing money?
- Why is the contract behind programme but making money?

Note that if the site is making money and is in front of programme this may be the result of either a good manager or the work being overpriced.

One of the tools used when trying to answer such questions is the cash flow. However, in order for cash flow to be used as a tool for monitoring and controlling production it is necessary to separate the cumulative curve into its respective sub-contractor, labour, materials and plant elements, as shown in figure 10.6.

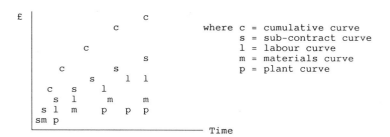

Figure 10.6   Cumulative cost/revenue curves for each resource

By doing this it is easier to locate the problem. The data may also be used to identify specific loss making elements in situations where the contract is making money overall. Improving profit on a job that is making money is often ignored although it is as important as rectifying a loss making situation.

References
1 FELLOWS, R, LANGFORD, D, NEWCOMBE, R, and URRY, S, *Construction management in practice*, Longmans 1983, pp 207–211.
2 OXLEY, R, and POSKITT, J, *Management techniques applied to the construction industry*, fourth edition, Collins 1986, pp 252.

Questions
1 (a)   Explain why a cash flow forecast will predict an apparent initial loss when cost is compared with income.

   (b)   Describe the measures which a contractor can implement in order to improve this cash flow position.

2 Distinguish between cash flow forecasts prepared by builders for their own purposes and those required by clients.

3 Describe the process of producing a cash-flow forecast for a project and indicate how a contractor can control income and expenditure.

4 Explain how an S-curve of anticipated cumulative value can be produced from a priced bill of quantities.

Comment on the use of S-curves in monitoring the progress of a project.

11   Tender Finalisation

Tender analysis   Tender analysis is carried out by both the QS and the builder. However, the purpose of the analysis differs between the two parties. This is because the QS is concerned with advising the client which builder to select whereas each builder is concerned with validating the details of their own estimate in order to produce a successful bid which, if successful, can be executed within the bid constraints. The analysis undertaken by the two is also different, not only due to these individual needs but also as a result of the difference in data available to each.

Analysis by the quantity surveyor

Initially the QS is provided with the tender price of each bidder but unless a tender breakdown is requested, as in the case where fully priced BQs are to be submitted with the tender, the data available is limited to a variety of lump sums (the bid prices). This is particularly so with tenders based on plan and specification although to overcome this the builder may be asked to submit a priced schedule of the work.

On receipt of the tender forms the QS will review the bids in order to report to the client. This involves the ranking of the bidders, from the lowest to the highest price. The ranking is more complicated where both time and price are competitive elements.

The purpose of this initial analysis is to determine:

- the number of bids, if any, which fall within the design budget
- the extent to which the bids are bunched to assess their competitiveness
- note a bid which is well below the bunch as this may contain errors which could compromise the builder and later cause problems for the client
- which is the most suitable tender for possible acceptance, in which case the priced BQ will be called for analysis
- which bidders will be asked to submit a priced BQ should the initial favourable tender not be acceptable.

On receipt of the selected builder's priced BQ a more detailed analysis is carried out. Any unusual pricing features that are found to exist need to be recorded and included in the tender report. This analysis will involve checking:

- the BQ section totals, contained in the bill summary page, to establish whether they are generally in line with his pretender figures. This helps to assess whether sections are realistically priced and ensures that there is no evidence of price loading.
- certain individual rates to ascertain the level of pricing, the pricing structure and that there are no pricing inconsistencies which could lead to valuation problems during the contract
- that arithmetic and pricing errors have not occurred. Those that are found are recorded so that these and other alterations (reduction bills) to the tender can be carried out to enable the contract sum to be finalised for subsequent entry into the contract agreement.

Analysis by the builder

Tender analysis is necessary for builders in order to provide management with adequate information, relating to the estimate, upon which to base a tender. This involves breaking down the estimate into sections meaningful to management, these being the general cost centres of the organisation. The breakdown is normally presented in the form of a final summary, an example of which is given in the Code of Estimating Practice.

The final summary contains totals, discounts and adjustments for the following:

- builder's own work – labour, materials plant and sub-contractors
- PC and provisional sums, daywork and contingency
- project overheads
- value related items not included elsewhere
- provision for the addition of margin when decided by management.

The data is required in this manner because management can relate to these sums as they correspond to the form they are incurred. By also expressing these sums as percentages, for example labour as a percentage of both the total value of own work and the total job value, valid comparisons with the respective figures from past tenders and completed projects can be achieved before any decisions are made.

Estimator's report   The estimator must prepare a report for management consideration, summarising all the relevant informa-

tion as outlined in the CIOB published COEP. This report should
also include:

- net cost estimate, supporting quotations and pricing
  philosophy, cost significant items including reservations
  about the pricing of items, especially those of a unique nature.
- tender analysis
- summary of project overheads
- risks and uncertainties associated with any aspect of the job
  including those relating to documentation, production,
  contract and cash flow
- preliminary tender enquiry form
- consultants and site visit reports
- production programme and network
- method statement
- site layout details
- cash flow details
- details of alternative methods and project overheads that
  have been considered but discarded on the basis of inferior
  time and/or cost solutions. This information will allow the
  tendering team to convince management that the correct
  solution for the successful completion of the project has been
  formulated.
- points which may give rise to qualification of the tender.

Adjudication   This is the meeting during which management
consider all the information generated during the tender period
including the estimator's report, tender documentation and related
instructions, from which the tender sum will be established. The
management conducting the meeting may consist of the managing
director (MD) and/or the commercial director or all directors. The
meeting is attended by those that have been involved in producing
data/reports although the actual staff that is invited to attend the
meeting will vary between organisations.

Those staff that may contribute to the meeting include estimator,
planner, contracts manager, accountant (if not a director), and
possibly buyer. Large organisations may also consider major
tenders initially at regional level followed by a further meeting with
top management at head office. In very formal environments an
agenda of the points to discuss is likely to be set. If this is not the case
it is advisable to have an informal checklist of items to be addressed
to ensure all matters are covered.

Builders conduct their adjudication meetings in different ways
although the most effective approach is for the tender team to
describe each facet of the tender data in the form of a presentation.
The use of visual material is recommended here. This allows a
speaker to make reference to:

- *wall displays* – programme, network, drawings and cash flow
- *overhead projector displays* – site layout, cost and time implications of alternative methods, sketches of design details that need to be referred to, calculations of labour levels and outputs and list of priced preliminary items.

Presentations supported by such visual aids not only enable management to absorb information more readily but also increases the amount of information that can be absorbed. This arrangement also allows management to question the team, on completion of the presentation, in more detail. The presentation must be short but to the point and follow a coherent path. Such presentations may take the following format:

- introduction to cover general aspects such as job title, type of job, location, parties involved, approximate value, duration and the like
- sequence in which the project is to be built
- method and approach
- site layout
- site overheads
- network sequence and logic
- production programme
- contract conditions
- estimating approach and any unique features together with the need for qualifying the tender
- net cost final summary
- cash flow
- risks that have been identified
- report on competitors and results of own previous bids.

Management function   The task of converting an estimate is that of management, once acquainted with the details of the project. It is therefore the responsibility of management to validate the estimate and production plan before making any decisions. The validation involves:

Estimate   – review the net cost final summary and evaluate resource total levels
– review general pricing levels within the estimate
– review individual rates for own work
– review the additions made to both nominated and domestic sub-contractors together with those for dayworks and the like
– review the cost of site overheads
– increase or reduce prices where it is considered appropriate

Planning   – a review of all the aspects of production is carried out including associated matters such as cash flow and cost alternatives
         – amendments to the plan where it is considered necessary. Where cost and cash flow are affected by such amendments these too must be subsequently revised by those responsible.

Having discussed all matters arising from the estimator's report, including supporting data, it is then necessary to assess the builder's overall financial commitment associated with the project. To facilitate this the following points need to be addressed:

- current turnover
- current financial commitment and cash flow of the whole organisation
- interest rates on loans
- current resource commitment
- the effects on the above if this bid is successful
- cash flow
- recovery of general overheads and profit
- recovery of site overheads
- requirement of a bond
- proportion of own work
- the need to purchase additional cost significant plant especially if of a specialist nature
- payment arrangements and intervals
- retention percentage and maximum value
- liquidated damages
- firm price allowance or fluctuating price and method of recovery
- credit facilities offered by suppliers and subcontractors
- risk and uncertainty.*

* Both *risk* and *uncertainty* relate to events which may occur in the future. However, *risk* refers to events for which a possible outcome may be predicted. For example, the exact amount of time lost to adverse weather conditions and the dates such conditions will take place cannot be known in advance. As such conditions are not rare in Britain there is a high probability that they will occur. By referring to past records it is possible to make a suitable time allowance in advance of the event taking place. The accuracy of the predicted allowance is unknown until the event takes place, thus the builder takes a risk. *Uncertainty* refers to events for which a possible outcome cannot be predicted. For example, the workforce may take strike action. This action is possible but there is a low probability that such an event will take place. Irrespective of whether or not the action can be predicted it would be impossible to predict the effects as the action may for example last either one day or one year.

Risks to be considered at the adjudication meeting include:

- past working relations with the client and any of his consultants
- aspects of construction that may cause problems such as culverts, high water table, watercourses, high quality internal and external finish required, complicated design details and unique features
- aspects of the contract conditions that may cause problems such as working restrictions, suspension of work at any time, builder's design portion, firm price, very short contract duration
- shortage in the supply of resources (labour and materials)
- costs through delays and disruption which are inherent when the design is incomplete
- problems that occur when tender documents are contradictory or vague
- errors inherent with plan and specification work
- unforeseen costs associated with alteration and refurbishment work
- adequacy and accuracy of the overall cost in relation to the type and nature of the project.

The first problem which arises when considering risk is identifying the risk items. From the short list above some are easily identified. However, others are not easy to identify. Also some cannot be easily identified as the item of risk may change with each job especially the unforeseen costs on alteration work. Other risks may only be identified if experienced on other projects.

If the first problem is overcome then the second problem must then be resolved. This involves evaluating the risk. With the exception of firm price and possibly resource shortages, quantifying the cost implications of risks is not only difficult but could result in the tender sum being less competitive.

After considering the financial commitment the management must balance the cost implications with both the strength of competition and the desire to win the job. The tender margin is thus decided and the tender sum agreed together with any qualifications to the tender. Specific instructions as to how margin should be allocated to the estimate must be stated by management. This is important irrespective of whether a priced BQ is required to be submitted with the tender form as it saves time in circumstances where a priced BQ is to be submitted at a later date. Once all the business is concluded the meeting is brought to a close.

The final responsibility of management is to vet and sign the tender form so that it can be returned to the architect within the submission deadline. In some organisations the chief estimator or contracts manager may have the authority to sign the tender form, especially where management may not always be available.

Qualifying tenders   The code of procedure for single stage selective tendering, item 4.4, states that tenderers should not qualify their tenders. Whilst builders risk invalidating a tender submission by qualifying a tender there are circumstances in which this is necessary. Qualification here relates to a bidder altering the basis of his tender price such that it effectively differs from that basis set out in the tender documents. The qualification may be either set out on the form of tender or by attaching an accompanying letter to the tender form.

The qualification may be a note explaining such matters as: the tender is based on a fluctuating price as opposed to firm, an alternative specification has been used for part of the work, an item of work has been omitted because no one is prepared to quote, a reduced tender period is offered (though this may be at a higher price) and the like. Builders are sometimes put into a compromising situation and need to qualify their tenders in order to safeguard their interests.

For example, consider the builder who could not obtain a sub-contract price for specialist work of an abnormal nature. Because other bidders were having the same problem the architect asked all bidders to inform him of the name of a firm willing to price the work, should one be found, so that other bidders could be notified. At five forty five on the evening prior to the day of tender submission – deadline being nine o'clock in the morning – the architect telephoned the builder with the name of a sub-contractor. As the sub-contractor could not be contacted that evening the architect agreed to give all bidders the sub-contractor's price. The architect had no further details such as discount, firm/fluctuating price, scope of the work within the price and numerous technical matters. The architect was expecting bidders to take a risk with the sub-contract price but was not willing to accept the price and include it as either a prime cost or provisional sum. The builder therefore submitted a tender exclusive of the sub-contract work, the tender form being qualified by a note to that effect.

Final adjustments and tender submission   Following the adjudication meeting the estimator must make all the cost adjustments to the estimate that have been decided by management. This includes adjustments for:

  – savings arising from late quotations and adjustments for discounts

- revision of prices following any changes to the all-in hourly labour rates, outputs and site overheads
- general price changes to sections of work
- additions for mark-up.

As it is impractical at this stage to make the actual changes to the unit rates, unless the estimate is on computer, the estimator will make a lump sum adjustment to the estimate based on the difference between the total of all increases and the total of all reductions. Should a price BQ have to be submitted with the tender a limited number of items and corresponding page and section totals may be changed depending on how much time remained for submitting the tender. As soon as the calculations are complete the tender form is completed ready for signing and subsequent delivery.

Action after tender submission   Once the tender is signed and dispatched the tender value and date of submission is recorded in the tenders submitted register along with its allotted job reference number. When the builder is notified of the tender result the success or failure is also recorded in the tenders submitted register. Should the tender be unsuccessful all documents and data relating to the tender are bound together, the job number stamped on clearly and then filed for future reference. If the tender is successful and a priced BQ is called then the estimator arranges for a fully priced BQ to be submitted and later will deal with any price adjustments arising from errors found by the quantity surveyor. The notification of tender prices submitted by all bidders enables an analysis of the organisation's bidding performance to be carried out.

Other tasks that may be subsequently performed include:

- vetting contract documents before signing to ensure there are no changes from the tender documents
- issuing relevant tender documentation to those parties within the organisation involved in the project post contract
- making regular visits to site, if possible, to reconcile the decisions made during the tender period with events on site
- on completion of the project the final account and total cost should be reconciled with the tender cost data to help improve future estimates.

Questions

1 Describe the factors to be included in an estimator's report to management, and draw up a standard agenda for an adjudication meeting.

2 Describe the information to be included in an estimator's report to management for an adjudication meeting. Outline the aims of the final summary of costs.

3 (a) Explain why management needs a detailed breakdown of an estimate total before considering adjustments for mark-up.

  (b) Identify the components of the estimate summary which can readily be adjusted and describe the likely effects of such adjustments on the subsequent management of the project.

4 Analyse the factors considered by management at the tender stage to establish a profit margin.

12 Bidding Strategy

Purpose of bidding
The term bidding refers generally to the tendering activity of a builder's organisation, namely the production of the highest possible tender sum which will win the work and contribute to annual profit requirements. As this is traditionally the major method of obtaining work, the lowest bid being normally accepted, the bidding strategy of any building organisation is important. Bidding strategy relates to the method used by a builder to calculate his mark-up in a competitive situation and relies heavily on the analysis of past performance.

Because the actions of other bidders is difficult to predict the outcome of any particular bid is uncertain. This often leads to unrealistically low tender prices and often hinders future planning within some organisations. Whilst very low prices are to be expected within a very competitive building industry they often result in poor building work and claims for additional payment. To avoid these circumstances builders need to be able to predict the outcome of a bid with more certainty.

The bidding objectives of a builder are to:

- determine the chance of winning the job in order to justify preparing a detailed tender
- increase the chances of winning jobs
- maximise expected profit
- minimise expected losses where unrealistically low bids are undertaken
- realise an adequate return for the level of risk to be taken
- secure capital growth
- provide a smooth workload.

Builders strive to meet these objectives irrespective of the external forces that may prevail. For example, account must be taken of market, political and economic trends together with the effect these have on other competitors.

Theory of bidding Bidding strategies concern the relationships between the levels of mark-up, estimating accuracy, estimating costs and the number of competitors which in turn influence the probability of winning a job with a given profit. Here profit relates to that which is anticipated but not necessarily realised on completion of the job.

Mark-up

As builders' costs are similar the main variable in bids is the mark-up. Thus, any mark-up must be high enough to achieve a suitable level of profit whilst be low enough to win the job. High mark-ups will attach a lower level of success, or probability of winning, than low mark-ups. Therefore, in theory as the level of profit increases so the probability of winning reduces.

In order to determine the level of mark-up for a particular job it is necessary to predict the mark-up of competitors. The percentage mark-up of a competitor is achieved by analysing the builder's own previous bid data together with that of the competitor:

$$\text{Competitor's mark-up} = \frac{\text{competitors bid less own estimated cost}}{\text{own estimated cost}} \times 100$$

Probability of winning

Probability is expressed numerically from zero to one. Thus, 100% chance of success would have a probability of 1, whereas 2% chance (very little chance) of success would have a probability of 0.02. The range of probability is likely to fall between these two extremes.

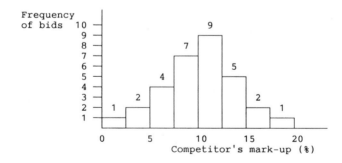

Figure 12.1   Distribution of competitor's mark-up

The probability of winning a job against a particular competitor is achieved by calculating that competitor's mark-up, using the data collected from as many bid situations involving the builder and the competitor. A frequency distribution, figure 12.1, is then produced to show the number of times the builder was beaten by the competitor at the given levels of mark-up. The builder's own performance in relation to that of the competitor is then converted

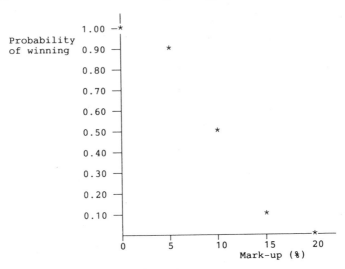

Figure 12.2   Probability of winning curve

into probabilities and when plotted against mark-up a curve is produced, figure 12.2, showing the probability of winning with any given mark-up.

From figure 12.1 the sum of the numbers above each frequency bar gives a total of 31 occasions when the builder competed against the particular competitor. The success of each organisation is as follows:

with own mark-up of 5% the competitor on average wins 3 or 9.68% (sum of frequencies to the left of the 5% mark), the builder wins 28 or 90.32%. The builder's probability of winning being 0.90

with own mark-up of 10% the competitor on average wins 14 or 45.16% (sum of frequencies to the left of the 10% mark), the builder wins 17 or 54.84%. The builder's probability of winning being 0.55

with own mark-up of 15% the competitor wins 28 or 90.30%, the builder wins 3 or 9.70%. The builder's probability of winning being 0.10

with own mark-up of 20% the competitor on average wins all 31 bids and the builder's probability of winning is zero.

From figure 12.2 the probability of winning against the competitor for any given mark-up can be determined for consideration by management before bidding decisions are made – assuming that the estimator has sufficient time to spend on this.

A number of competitors

Bidding situations normally involve more than one competitor. Therefore the probability of winning curve must, where possible, be derived from data concerning the bid performance of all the known bidders. Where the performance of other bidders is not known then the probability of winning with a given mark-up is more difficult to determine. However, many attempts have been made to equate the probability of winning with a number of competitors.[1] These are mathematical solutions which relate the chance of winning at a given mark-up to the probability of beating every competitor:

probability of A winning = probability of beating B × probability of beating C × probability of beating D × probability of beating E, F, G, ...

Profit optimisation

By equating given levels of profit with their respective probability of winning the most favourable contribution for each job can be derived. The most favourable contribution is that which maximises the expected profit of a job. This is referred to as the probable profit contribution (PPC), as shown in table 12.1, the varying levels of contribution being used to determine the optimum bid.

Net cost £th	Profit %	Bid value £th	Probability of winning (assumed)	PPC
500	− 2	475	1.00	− 2
500	0	500	0.90	0
500	1	505	0.75	0.75
500	2	510	0.50 (optimum)	1.00
500	3	515	0.25	0.75
500	4	520	0.15	0.60
500	5	525	0.07	0.35
500	6	530	0.01	0.06

Table 12.1   Probable profit contribution: showing optimum bid

A contribution curve can be produced by plotting the PPC against bid value.[2] The apex (highest point) of the curve denotes the optimum bid value. The curve may then be used to consider alternative bid values either side of the optimum. Also the effects of increasing numbers of competitors can be assessed. Note that as competition increases the probability of winning reduces. This results in lower bids at a reduced optimum level. Here, the PPC curve moves to the left with the apex at a lower point.

Limitations within bidding strategies

In practice all competitors are faced with the same problems in that each will produce a unique bid level for every tendering situation in order to undercut others that are doing likewise. This is why the outcome of bidding is often viewed as a matter of chance. Whilst bidding theory, as a mathematical calculation, is not widely used by builders the same factors are considered. One reason why so many bidding strategy models have practical limitations is the lack of scope for applying subjective judgement, this being necessary in order to capitalise on experience and gut feeling. Other limitations relate to the assumptions that have to be made in order to limit a model to a manageable number of variables. Typical assumptions are:

– builder's own estimate is accurate
– competitor's estimate is accurate
– competitor's estimates are the same as the builder's own
– competitor's mark-up/bid strategy is constant
– chances of winning is an average, based on long term performance.

In general builders are not convinced that a theoretical approach to bidding will provide better results than the more conventional approach. As the perfect bidding strategy has not been developed there will always be those that seek that final goal.

Estimating

The accuracy of an estimate influences the true value of a bid to the extent that the bid may be more or less than the sum of the actual cost and mark-up. Therefore, if the work is overpriced the bid will be higher than need be. Such a bid has a reduced chance of success if other bidders have not overpriced the work.

The cost of estimating associated with each bid is recovered on the jobs that are won. Thus, the level of abortive tendering will influence the bid price. How this affects the tender sum for a builder who incurs estimating costs equal to 1.5% of the contract value is shown as follows:

where the probability of winning is 0.5 the average success ratio is 1:2. The estimating cost of the two bids is $2 \times 1.5\%$. Therefore, the one successful job must include 3% to cover estimating costs of that job together with the abortive estimating costs of the unsuccessful bid where the probability of winning is 0.1 the average success ratio is 1:10. The estimating cost of the ten bids is 10 × 1.5%. Therefore, the one successful job must include 15% to cover all ten jobs.

Margin lost in competition concept   The mark-up which is applied at tender in unlikely to be achieved on completion of a project. The margin lost in competition (MLC) concept is intended to explain this phenomenom and relies on the fact that there exists inaccuracies in estimating.

Every estimator has a different level of estimating accuracy therefore a number of estimators will produce a range of cost estimates in any bid situation. Further, there is usually a range of possible costs associated with each job. Each estimator is concerned with predicting the job costs that will be incurred by their respective organisation. The management of each firm then applies their own level of mark-up to the cost estimate.

Therefore, anticipated net costs and mark-ups will vary. Due to the existence of these variables the effects of differing levels of estimating inaccuracies are difficult to assess, the root cause of any affect being uncertain. To overcome the variables problem the MLC concept assumes that the only variance is the accuracy of estimating.

How close a net cost estimate is to a builder's likely, or completely accurate cost, varies with the level of accuracy achieved. As the accuracy of the estimate is not certain the net cost is expressed as:

likely cost + or − A%

where: likely cost = actual cost

+ or − A% = the accuracy of the estimate in terms of the percentage above or below the likely cost.

The A% range for any given group of bidders may fall above, below or above and below the likely cost. However, because the lowest bid normally wins the chances of winning with a likely cost + A% are reduced. This is particularly so when there are many bidders because the chance of likely cost − A% bids being prepared is increased. Those builders with a negative estimating accuracy have a better chance of winning, the greater the − A% the higher the probability of success.

By producing a distribution of winning bids, all with the same mark-up (earlier assumption) the mean of the winning bids can be found. As successful bids are probably the likely cost − A% the mean of winning bids occurs at a point between the likely cost and the mean likely bid (likely cost plus mark-up). The difference between the mean likely bid value and the mean winning bid value is the sum which is lost in competition.[3] Because the actual costs incurred have to be paid for by the builder any shortfall between actual and estimated costs must come from the mark-up. Hence the achieved mark-up is likely to be less than that applied at tender.

Break even mark-up concept   This concept follows on from the MLC concept, supporting the view that a number of estimators will produce a range of estimates which equal + or − A%, the bidder with a likely cost −A% having the best chance of winning.

Thus, over a large number of bids the average difference between applied and achieved margins is the average difference between likely and estimated costs. This is called the break even mark-up (BEM). It therefore follows that a winning bid with zero profit results in the builder making a loss equal to the −A%. This loss increases as the number of competitors increases. Therefore in order to break even the break even mark-up must be applied, the level of mark-up depending on both the number of competitors and the estimating accuracy.

The effects, on bidding, which results from increasing estimating accuracy have been investigated.[4] The investigation involved testing bid outcomes, by simulation, for different levels of accuracy and different numbers of bidders. In order to reach any conclusions the simulation variables were restricted to accuracy and number of bidders. The hypotheses and conclusions of the investigation are as follows:

hypotheses – If a builder improves estimating accuracy will this affect:
 – his ability to win jobs?
 – his profits?
 – any benefits if competitors do likewise?

Conclusions:
 – achieved margins are improved if accuracy is improved
 – by improving accuracy to maintain turnover the builder must either:
  – reduce applied mark-up OR
  – increase the number of bids OR
  – partly reduce markup and partly increase bids
 – achieved margins are greater than previous if all competitors improve their estimating accuracy.

Bidding models   Bidding models attempt to predict the chances of winning against either all bidders or the lowest bidder (low bid).

The all bidders models tend to be very complex as they need to take account of the probabilities of each bidder in combination with the influence each has overall. For instance, the Gates model for known competitors is:

$$p = \frac{1}{[(1 - pa)/pa] + [(1 - pb)/pb] + [(1 - pc)/pc] + [(1 - pd. \ldots}$$

where: pa = probability of beating A
pb = probability of beating B
pc = probability of beating C
pd = probability of beating D.

The low bid model is less complex as the builder needs only to analyse the chances of beating one bidder, as shown in figures 12.1 and 12.2. The difficulty is predicting the likely lowest bidder.

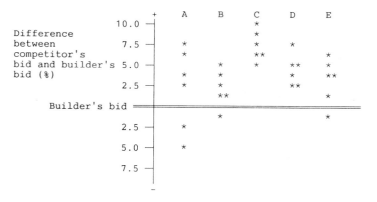

Where * represents competitors' bids and ===== represents the builder's bid.

Figure 12.3   Bid performance record

A more traditional model is based on recording a builder's performance with that of his competitors, as shown in figure 12.3. This involves calculating the percentage differences between the builder's past bids and those of other bidders. The outcome of a specific bid may then be assessed by predicting competitors bid levels. The performance data may be classified to provide a performance profile for each individual competitor on different types of work.

The bid performance record shows that for job **A** the builder was 5% below the winning bid and 2.5% below the next lowest. The builder submits a more competitive bid for job **B** but is beaten by 1.25%. Job **C** is won by the builder but having over estimated the strength of competition leaves 5% on the table. Job **D** is also won with 2.5% on the table. Unfortunately job **D** is lost by 1.25% due to increased competition.

Efficiency of bidding models   The efficiency of any strategy model is measured by the number of jobs won, the achieved profit and the money left on the table. The efficiency of a model, perfect efficiency being 100%, may be calculated as follows:

$$\text{Efficiency of the model} = \frac{\text{Profit}}{\text{Profit} + \text{money left on table}} \times \% \text{ jobs won.}$$

Where: – profit = total profit for all jobs won
  – money left on table = sum, for all jobs won, of the difference between the low competitor bid and the successful builder's bid.

$$\text{Profit efficiency} = \frac{\text{Total profits of winning bids}}{\text{Maximum possible profits}}$$

where max. possible profits is the sum, for all jobs won, of the difference between the low competitor bid and the builder's net cost.

Optimum profit
efficiency per job = Profit efficiency $\times (1 - \%$ age of jobs won).

References

1 SKITMORE, M, *Contract bidding in construction*, Longmans 1989, pp 179–182.
2 FELLOWS, R, LANGFORD, D, NEWCOMBE, R, and URREY, S, *Construction management in practice*, Longmans 1983, pp 221–222.
3 HARRIS, F, and McCAFFER, R, *Modern construction management*, second edition, Granada 1983, pp 226–227.
4 McCAFFER, R, 'Is there an economic case for more accurate estimating?, Estimating for the civil engineering and building industries', Proceedings of conferences held at Loughborough University of Technology, Northwood 1974, pp 7–13.

Questions

1 Discuss the ways in which a company's bidding strategy may be affected by a comprehensive evaluation of its own tender performance and that of its competitors.

2 Discuss how the following may affect the level of a contractor's tender:
   (a) an evaluation of previous tender results.
   (b) a consideration of competitive conditions.
   (c) the quality of project information.

3 A building company can assess its tender performance if it has prepared consistent net estimates and applied constant additions for overheads and profit over a significant period.
   Discuss this statement.

4 A local authority direct labour organisation is becoming increasingly involved in competitive tendering and needs to develop an effective bidding strategy.
   (a) Explain the need for a period of consistent prices and mark-up in order to evaluate tender performance.
   (b) Discuss the elements of a bidding strategy which should be considered by the local authority.

13 Computers in Construction

Historical developments The first generation of computers were developed between 1944 and 1955. These were very large but slow machines. Breakdowns were frequent as the valves operating the systems constantly overheated. Maintenance was high, due to the excessive amount of time spent tracking and rectifying faults caused by the constant overheating. Data was inputted by use of coded punch cards.

The use of transistors in lieu of valves allowed the second generation of computers, 1956 to 1963, to be smaller. These machines had improved reliability and enhanced processing power. A major advance in data input was achieved during this period as mathematical and English (PASCAL and FORTRON) languages were introduced. Data was inputted by use of magnetic tapes.

The third generation of computers were in use between 1964 and 1970, incorporating integrated circuits (IC) engraved on silicon slices or chips. This technological revolution opened up the way for further advances in miniaturisation, reliability and cost reductions.

The fourth generation of computers, from 1971 to date, incorporated very large scale integrated circuits (VLSI) able to hold up to approximately 1000 components.

During the early nineteen sixties organisations within the building industry started to invest in computers. Because of the size of these earlier machines the hardware and software occupied valuable floor space within buildings. In some institutions whole floors were devoted to computers. The rooms in which they were housed needed to be dust free and kept at a constant temperature and humidity level. Further, computing experts and technicians were needed to operate and maintain the systems.

The high capital cost together with the storage and operating costs limited their use as only the large organisations could afford to make such an investment. Another factor limiting computer use was the absence of application software. All the programs were devised for the batch processing of accountancy, payroll and similar functions. This meant that data input was carried out when batches of data was collected. As data was dealt with in batches the input and output was a time consuming process, data retrieval often being too late to use for decision making.[1]

Mini computers were introduced following the development of the micro chip. These computers were smaller and cheaper than the mainframes. Minis were similar to mainframes but with less circuitry and therefore much smaller. This advance allowed some smaller firms to acquire the technology. However, whilst programs were gradually being developed for building applications they were limited in complexity and mainly produced by individual firms for their own use.

By the late seventies micro computers had been developed. These revolutionised the computing industry as they were cheap, reliable and small enough to fit on a work desk. As the demand for computers increased, both for industry and home use, the unit cost reduced drastically. Computer applications also increased to meet the needs of consumers. As a result, systems are now available to suit the aspirations and budgets of most firms.

Computers now in use The current situation is that mainframe, mini and micro computers are all available. However, the difference between them is constantly reducing with the development of more powerful small computers:

Mainframe computers

Mainframes have a large capacity for multi use of terminals, different application software and peripherals. They operate on hard disks which have huge storage facilities thereby enabling numerous complex packages to be stored for immediate access by a number of users. The advantages of a mainframe are firstly that economies in costs are achieved as the number of terminals increases and secondly the memory capability is vast.

Because mainframes are so powerful large amounts of information are required to keep them busy. Thus, computer analysts are often required to sort out these huge data banks. Where multi use is excessive at any one time some programs will cause the system to slow down. Serious problems may also arise with a mainframe should there be a breakdown. A data back-up system is therefore necessary should the system crash due to failure. If the mainframe is out of action then all use of the computer is lost. This may be critical and/or costly if effective manual systems cannot be implemented immediately.

Mini computers

These have to a great extent taken the place of the mainframe computers, except in situations where major networks are required, as they perform the same function but are much cheaper and smaller. However, the advantages and disadvantages are common to both mainframes and minis.

Micro computers

The desk top or personal computers, including the portable versions, are stand alone in that they are self supporting systems. They are relatively cheap to buy, very reliable, fairly portable and have the capacity to run a small network with a limited number of different peripherals. Some micro computers facilitate data input by use of a cassette. These computer systems are of no use within the building industry. Other micro computers run off either twin floppy disks or one hard disk together with a floppy.

The twin floppy will cope with many but not all packages due to the limited memory space on a floppy disk. Further, with twin floppies, disks have to be interchanged regularly due to the fact that one package is likely to be contained in parts on a number of disks. Continuous disc interchanging will eventually distort or corrupt the data.

The hard disk drive machines are more versatile as more programs can be stored and accessed. As the hard disk is a fixture the chances of it becoming corrupted are greatly reduced. Generated data can be stored on either the hard or floppy disk. The floppy disk allows data to be transferred to another computer.

Whilst micro computers may have breakdown problems these are less severe as only an individual work station or user is likely to be affected, except where there is a general power failure within a building.

Some computer terminology   Some terms relating to the text are outlined as follows:

- *application software* – computer programs or packages
- *commercially available/dedicated software* – application software developed by and readily purchased from a software producer/house or retailer.
- *digitiser* – electronic board or unit which automatically generates dimensions/quantities from the movements of an electronic hand held cursor (puck with buttons or pen with activating switch) when traced over a scaled drawing mounted on the unit
- *hardware* – generally anything that can be touched, including the computer and peripherals but excluding software
- *in-house development/software* – development of a system/ software by the intended user (self development)
- *kimball tag* – modern equivalent of a punch card, containing sales data, used for instant data input
- *light pen* – electronic instant data input facility
- *modem (modulator/demodulator)* – digital/audio conversion of data for telephone relay

- *network* – multi use of terminals from a single computer or alternatively communication between computers
- *on line system* – computer linked to telephone relay by modem.
- *optical reader* – read and load text directly into computer
- *peripherals* – anything attached to the computer for input/output such as monitor screens, keyboards, disk drives, printers, plotters, optical readers, modems, digitisers and light pens
- *software* – programmes supplied on cassette tapes or floppy discs

Types of software The range of available software is varied and becoming more sophisticated. Software is also more user friendly through the use of visual, or drop down, menu and sub-menu options. Software falls into two categories, namely *general purpose* and *application*. These collectively enable most office tasks to be performed more efficiently. Because more data is generated by computers and as more use is made of the technology it is crucial that adequate back-up copies of all programs and data are kept. This avoids losing vast amounts of data through power loss or disc corruption. Power loss often occurs when an electrical appliance with a high wattage, eg a kettle, is connected to the same multiple socket as that for the computer.

General purpose business software

Word processing packages together with spread sheet (see worked examples[2]) and data base management systems are commonly used within the industry for letter/report writing and limited graphics and calculations, performing repetitive calculations or producing histograms/pie charts for data interpretation and data storage/manipulation respectively. Expert system shells are also available, whereby knowledge acquired from experts[3] is entered in as one or more logic sequences or rules which lead to outputs of possible outcomes and consequences. The expert system shell therefore facilitates the development of a form of artificial intelligence.

General purpose business software for word processing, spreadsheets and data bases are relatively cheap, although can be time consuming when creating a complicated spreadsheet or database. These packages have applications over a range of activities and are developed by users as a work tool, mainly to deal with repetitive processes and large volumes of data. There are a number of versions available, some of which are compatible. For instance, data from a spreadsheet may be linked to a database, alternatively histograms formed on a spreadsheet may be transferred to a word processing file. Further, as many versions are compatible with some application software they may be used to generate and feed data directly into these other programs.

Application software

Application software is now developed either solely by practitioners who have computing expertise or jointly by practitioners and computer experts. These experts may be employed full time or commissioned to produce a computer system. The range of software available covers most tasks that need to be performed within the building industry. These tasks include BQ production, design, planning/programming, builder's estimating, quantity surveyor's estimating/cost planning, cash flow, structural calculations, cut and fill, BCIS on line data and desktop publishing. Often these packages or systems have the facility to perform multiple tasks. For example, some:

- estimating packages include a facility for BQ production, sub-contractors data and valuations.
- planning packages include cash flow, pricing and valuations, cash flow and pricing being generated automatically. The better versions are flexible in the manner in which valuation data is inputted and therefore facilitate the practical approach as an option. Thus, with a four storey building the valuation input may simply be:

    - foundations complete
    - frame 60% complete
    - services 10% complete,

    OR data may be inputted by the usual reference to specific items or parts thereof.
- design packages generate quantities, BQs in various formats and BQ pricing, all automatically.

Where some of these packages have been produced by the same organisation they are likely to be compatible, for example a planning or BQ package may be used directly with an estimating package. However, as packages are often chosen on merit, not on their compatibility with other packages, there is virtually no compatibility across the full range of software currently in use. Unfortunately, as there is little compatibility generally between systems, the opportunity for greatly improving data flow, thus increasing efficiency, throughout the industry seems to have been lost. Whilst the FAX electronic mailing system has provided an improvement in data flow and communications it cannot compare with that of computer-to-computer transfer of larger volumes of data, from one office to another, via telephone relay.

Software sources   Computerised systems are developed either in-house or by independent software companies,[4] although in-house systems are often later sold commercially.

The merits of developing software in-house are:

- made to measure systems
- fully integrated systems which allow data transfer between all departments and possibly the linking of all regional offices
- modification to the system is possible
- in-house training.

However, the two major disadvantages are the length of time required to produce a working system and the associated high cost of development.

The merits of purchasing commercial software are:

- virtual immediate use with most systems
- often relatively cheap
- state of the art technology
- updated versions offered
- some minor modifications or additional functions may be available
- training available, although often at a cost
- experienced users to offer advice.

The main disadvantages are that integrated systems are excluded and the system may not carry all the necessary functions or may not be operated in the manner required by certain users.

Computer acquisition   Government policies and market forces have put pressure on public and private sector industries to be more cost effective, profitable and provide better value for money services. For many industries this has been partly, if not wholly, achieved through opportunities created by developments in information technology (IT).

The building industry has been slow to respond to the technology but is fast catching up due to the rapid increase in the number of computer uses and users. However, a high proportion of the industry is not making use of the technology. Firms within the industry generally fall into one of the following user categories:

- *no computers* – whether intending to do so or not
- computers acquired – seldom used and/or limited to accounts and general office use
- *computers acquired* – full use intended but prevented by lengthy and costly development programs aimed at achieving complex integrated systems

    – *fully computerised* – integrated or not, complex or not.

The reasons why firms are not computerised or do not make full use of the computers may be attributable to:

    – employers' and employees' reluctance to change
    – inadequate systems available for their requirements
    – cash limitations
    – lack of knowledge or experience to make decisions in the selection of a system.

Selecting a system may be very difficult especially when faced with a multitude of options. Thus, before any decisions are made it is necessary to identify and prioritise the functions required of a system. Each alternative system can then be evaluated by comparing performances against the firm's selection criteria.[5] Because management often have a different perception of selection criteria to that of the staff ultimately using a system it is important that the perceived criteria of all concerned are considered in any evaluation appraisal.

    Some points to consider when selecting a system are:

    – capital and running costs
    – computer approach to the task
    – level of automation
    – amount of data input required
    – level of control retained by the user
    – compatibility with other systems
    – amount of training.

Types of computer aided estimating systems   The types of computer aided estimating (CAE) systems are differentiated by their approach to estimating. The approaches consist of bill pricing, price book and analytical/operational estimating:

Bill pricing approach

These are very basic systems which allow input of both BQ quantities and pre-determined unit rates and incorporate a calculator function that automatically calculates item, page, section and summary totals. There is also a facility to add overheads and profit. The unit rates may be stored in the system's library for later retrieval or update. This type of system may be suitable for some small builders and sub-contractors where the range of items to be priced is limited. Such a system may also be of use to small builders who undertake minor work of a repetitive nature that does not necessitate the calculation of new rates on every occasion, especialy if prices for their work are reasonably constant.

Price book approach

These systems are more advanced than bill pricing in that unit rates are split into the labour, material and plant elements. This allows labour and plant constants and prices to be adjusted to suit the type of work being priced. Material prices are updated within the materials library. This, however, is the limit to which an estimator can alter any unit rate as the resources allocated to each item are fixed within the program. Such systems are therefore price books transferred onto a computer. Further, whilst the approach to estimating is limited the prices of such packages are very high compared to many systems which offer the estimator full estimating control.

Price book systems often have other facilities such as a percentage adjuster on each item for waste on materials, total value of waste, list of significant cost items for any required level of significance, mark-up allocation and resource/cost analysis. Early approximate estimates of jobs are possible by inputting the quantities from the BQ and calculating the total cost using the data file, this having been updated for the previous bid.

Analytical/operational estimating approach

Estimators require the freedom to allocate to an item any resource combination without restriction. This is because the resources required to carry out an activity on one job may not be suitable for the same activity on another job. Analytical estimating systems allow work to be priced with this level of freedom. Most systems are solely analytical in approach although a few systems also allow operational estimating. Other facilities within each system are similar to those within price book systems. Note that some systems also allow resource combinations, which have been allocated to any particular item, to be stored and later recalled for direct entry into subsequent estimates.

A typical system will have a library file for input/storage of every resource required by the user, such as:

- *labour* – bricklayer, joiner, ganger, labourer, steel fixer
- *material* – commons and facing bricks, blocks, sand, cement
- *plant* – mixer, excavator, lorry, dumper
- *sub-contractors* – plasterer, plumber, glazier
- *PC and provisional sums* – lift and electrical installations.

Separate sections within the library file are devoted to each resource type to facilitate the estimate analysis. Once the resources are entered into their individual compartments, these being numbered, within each section the library need only be amended or extended occasionally. Each resource may then be priced.

Estimating is facilitated in another section of the system. Part of the estimating process for each job is the transfer of the BQ data into the system. This may be done by the estimator as each item is priced. Alternatively, a junior may carry out the whole data transfer before the estimator commences. Note that some systems allow data input by an optical reader.

When pricing an item the estimator selects the resources to be allocated and retrieves these from the resource library by entering the allotted resource compartment numbers. The estimated unit quantities for materials and outputs for both labour and plant are then entered against each resource. The final estimating task is to allocate new resource prices where necessary. Any subsequent change to the estimate is then usually a minor operation due to the speed and accuracy of the calculator facility.

Benefits of CAE   The general benefits of a CAE system are summarised as follows:

- early estimates
- automatic calculation and recalculation facility
- identification of cost significant items
- late adjustments
- rate loading
- allocation of mark-up
- estimate analysis
- sensitivity analysis – different total cost solutions which result from alternative pricing and mark-up levels.

Future influences of computerisation   Computer technology provides the opportunity to rationalise traditional practices. This is partly realised when computer aided systems allow tasks to be performed faster than if carried out manually. Other than this, efficiency has been achieved through faster high powered machines, automation of calculations and the use of input peripherals such as a light pen, digitiser or mouse. The scope for further efficiencies in office procedures can be achieved by increased levels of automation within a system.

The majority of office taks may be classified[6] as either:

mechanistic based processes – those which involve the manipulation of known facts and applied in a predetermined manner for

which there exists a single outcome eg the measurement of building work in accordance with the RICS SMM
OR
judgement/expertise based processes – those which involve the manipulation of a range of known and assumed facts both selected by judgement and applied in a manner which may or may not be predetermined, for which there exists a range of possible outcomes, eg the pricing of building work.

Therefore, mechanistic based processes naturally allow for full automation within systems whereas judgement based processes do not. However, by incorporating an expert system within a judgement based system full automation can be facilitated.

The scope for further efficiencies in on-site production processes can also be achieved by increased levels of automation through the use of robotics.[7] Research and development associated with construction robotics are extensively pursued in both the USA and Japan.[8]

Future project leader? The role of project leaders is that of planning, organisation, management and control. As professionals from many disciplines have acquired these qualities the role of project leader is no longer exclusive to any one discipline. However, each discipline is aware that other disciplines are improving and expanding both their expertise and management control systems in order to make themselves the natural choice as leader.

For instance, there are currently two or three commercially available management systems which offer a sophisticated level of planning linked directly to resource requirements and costs, cash flow and financial appraisal. There are some top level contracts managers, with the overall knowledge and experience of the whole building process, who have the potential to make use of such computerised systems for overall control.

The choice of leader would be more simplified had it not been for the comprehensive range of application software now available to all disciplines. This availability has enabled some practitioners to acquire the skills of others and therefore create an overlap of services offered. However, the key to leadership is the analysis, synthesis and application of information rather than that of information production. Therefore, it is likely that a new breed of leaders will emerge rather than any one discipline rising above the others.

References

1 BARTON, P, *Information systems in construction management – principles and applications*, Batsford 1985, pp 6.

2 COOKE, B, and BALAKRISHNAN, SV, *Computer Spreadsheet applications in building and surveying, Macmillan 1985*

3 BRANDON, P S, 'The application of expert systems to quantity surveying', Computer aided learning in construction, Proceedings of conference held at Leeds Polytechnic in association with ADDSP, Leeds Polytechnic 1987, pp 73.

4 BETTS, M P, COOK, A E, and GRIFFITHS, B R, 'Computer aided estimating systems: An evaluation of user criteria': Part 1 'A pilot study', Brunswick Environmental Paper, no. 59, 1986.

5 COOK, A E, 'Selecting the right system', Construction Computing, Winter 1988/89, pp 26–27.

6 COOK, A E, 'Automation of computer aided systems, Computer aided learning in construction', Proceedings of conference held at Leeds Polytechnic in association with AHDSP, Leeds Polytechnic 1987, pp 139–140.

7 WARSZAWSKI, A, 'Application of robotics to building construction', CIB report, no. 90. International Council for Building Research, Studies and Documentation (Rotterdam) 1984.

8 KOSKELA, L, 'Construction industry towards the information society: The Japanese example', FACE report, no. 7, International Federation of Associations of Computer Users in Engineering, Architecture and Related Fields (Finland), 1985.

Questions

1 Compare a 'price book' database estimating package with an alternative computer aided method of generating rates for building work.

2 Compare the use of stand-alone desktop computers with the use of a share central computer facility for the estimating function.

3 Identify the advantages to the estimator in using computers in the preparation of reports, adjustments and contract budget.

4 The surveying department of a Direct Labour Organisation is considering the introduction of desktop computers to assist in valuing repetitive small works and repairs
    Identify the criteria to be considered in selecting software.

Abbreviations used in text

BCIS	Building Cost Information Service
BEC	Building Employers Confederation
BEM	break even mark-up
BPF	British Properties Federation
BQ	Bill of Quantities
BSI	British Standards Institution
CA	common arrangement
CAE	computer aided estimating
CF	cash flow
CFF	cash flow forecast
CIOB	chartered Institute of Builders
COEP	Code of Estimating Practice
CPI	co-ordinated project information
CSO	Central Statistical Office
DoE	Department of the Environment
DSO	direct services organisation
EEC	European Economic Community
HATS	Housing Action Trust
IFC	Intermediate Form of Contract
JCT	Joint Contracts Tribunal
MLC	margin lost in competition
NBS	National Building Specification
NES	National Engineering Specification
NJCBI	National Joint Council for the Building Industry
NSC	Nominated Sub-contract
NPV	net present value
PPC	probable profit contribution
PSA	Property Services Agency
QS	Quantity Surveyor
RIBA	Royal Institute of British Architects
RICS	Royal Institution of Chartered Surveyors
WRA	Working Rule Agreement
VAT	value added tax
VLSIC	very large scale integrated circuits

Index

Index